The Open University

U116

Environment: journeys through a changing world

Block 3
Nile limits

Parts 1–2

Pamela Furniss and Susan Fawssett

This publication forms part of the Open University course U116 *Environment: journeys through a changing world*. Details of this and other Open University courses can be obtained from the Student Registration and Enquiry Service, The Open University, PO Box 197, Milton Keynes MK7 6BJ, United Kingdom (tel. +44 (0)845 300 60 90; email general-enquiries@open.ac.uk).

Alternatively, you may visit the Open University website at www.open.ac.uk where you can learn more about the wide range of courses and packs offered at all levels by The Open University.

To purchase a selection of Open University course materials visit www.ouw.co.uk, or contact Open University Worldwide, Walton Hall, Milton Keynes MK7 6AA, United Kingdom for a brochure (tel. +44 (0)1908 858793; fax +44 (0)1908 858787; email ouw-customer-services@open.ac.uk).

The Open University
Walton Hall, Milton Keynes
MK7 6AA

First published 2009.

Edited and designed by The Open University.

Typeset by SR Nova Pvt. Ltd, Bangalore, India.

Printed and bound in the United Kingdom by Halstan Printing Group, Amersham.

ISBN 978 0 7492 2088 4

1.1

Contents

Introduction to Block 3 5

Part 1 Waters of the Nile 9

1 Introduction 11

2 Whose water is it? 15

Summary of Section 2 20

3 Water – a renewable resource 21

3.1 The water cycle 21

3.2 Renewable and non-renewable resources 22

3.3 Water quality 27

3.4 Water-borne disease 32

3.5 Water systems 35

Summary of Section 3 38

4 Ways of getting water 39

Summary of Section 4 40

5 Ways of using water 41

5.1 Irrigation 44

5.1.1 Salinisation and waterlogging 47

5.2 Fisheries 48

5.3 Transport, tourism and wildlife 49

Summary of Section 5 51

6 Dams 52

6.1 Costs and benefits of dams 52

6.2 Two dams compared 56

6.2.1 High Aswan Dam 56

6.2.2 Bujagali Falls 61

6.3 Water level in Lake Victoria 68

6.4 Alternatives to big dams 71

Summary of Section 6 73

7 Getting enough? 74
7.1 Problems ... 74
7.2 ... and solutions? 77
Summary of Section 7 81
Summary of Part 1 82
Answers to SAQs 83
References 88

Part 2 The forest is ours! 91
1 Introduction 93
2 A place for wildlife 94
2.1 What is conservation? 95
2.2 Why conserve our biophysical environment? 96
2.3 How is conservation done? 98
Summary of Section 2 103
3 Bwindi Impenetrable National Park case study 104
Summary of Part 2 105
References 106
Acknowledgements 107

Introduction to Block 3

Welcome to Block 3. The presentation of this block differs from Blocks 1 and 2 in that it has only two parts rather than three or four. It is also highly interactive and much of the material and learning is presented on the course DVD.

This block journeys to one of the most diverse regions of the world – the Nile river basin. Here there are baking deserts and rich tropical forests, high mountains and lowland marshes, densely populated cities and vast areas devoid of any type of human development. Linking all of these is the River Nile, the longest river in the world, which flows nearly 6700 km from the mountains of Rwanda and Ethiopia through forests, lakes and desert to its delta on the Mediterranean Sea near Cairo.

It is an area of great contrasts – of climate, of ecosystem and of resource availability. This block will explore some of these contrasts and particularly focus on the effects they have on the people living in this region. Many of the people of the Nile region live in conditions where access to the means for basic survival can be a constant challenge. Having access to water that is safe to drink, enough food, adequate shelter, basic sanitation – all of which many people in the developed world tend to take for granted – are the primary concerns for many of the people of the Nile. In situations where these resources are in limited supply, and where the demands are great, then conflict – one of the themes of this block – is a likely result. Conflict between people may occur at a range of scales, from between individuals at a local level through to conflict between countries at international level. It may range from a difference of opinion through to armed warfare. At any level, when people are in conflict, their priorities are usually meeting their own needs and furthering their own interests, often at the expense of others and at the expense of their environment. Environmental protection and sustainability are issues that are frequently well down the agenda in these circumstances. This can create other, rather different, forms of conflict between people and their environment and other living things. Meeting the demands of the human population can lead to damage or destruction of habitats at the cost of the plants and animals that live there. As the number of people in the world rises, these pressures on our environment will increase.

The resulting human impact on the environment has another side, however, and that is the impact that the environment, and particularly environmental change, can have on human lives. The uncertainty of global climate change can put even greater stress on people already struggling to survive, especially the poor, who are least able to adapt to changing circumstances.

These are complex problems. This block will attempt to unpick some of these issues and demonstrate that, although there are no easy solutions, there are approaches that can be successful in meeting human needs without causing lasting damage to the environment. These approaches to conflict resolution frequently rely on cooperation between the people involved, and this is a second theme for the block.

Block 3 focuses on two main issues – water resources and wildlife conservation. In different ways, both these issues are concerned with the use of resources and the impact that resource use has on our environment. A simple definition of resources might be 'things that we use'. This clearly encompasses a vast range of different types of 'thing' and there are different ways of categorising them. Natural resources are things that we get from the Earth and they are sometimes classified into physical or biological resources. Physical resources include fossil fuels, rocks, minerals and water. Biological resources are the plants and animals. But is that all? What else do we 'use'? What about the land underneath your house or the roads you travel on? What about the air you breathe? What about wildlife and scenery? Or the park or woods you might take a walk in? And what are their constituent parts? Plants and animals certainly, but also soil and space and the complex interactions between all the components that go together to make what we understand as a wood or a park. These are all things we use in one way or another – not only to meet our fundamental needs for food, shelter and warmth but also to meet less tangible needs associated with the quality of our lives. They are resources that we value for their aesthetic rather than material benefits. The term 'environmental resources' is sometimes used to encompass these as well as physical and biological resources.

Apart from the 'things', the other component in my simple definition of resources is 'we', the human race. Resources, in the sense used here, are a human-centred concept and are defined in terms of their use by human beings. Our use of resources depends on who 'we' are. The resources I use are probably not entirely the same as yours and certainly not the same as, say, an Inuit hunter, an Australian farmer or a Tokyo business executive. If you asked each of these people for a list of the resources they used, you would get very different lists. They would not only demonstrate the differing locations, lifestyles and economic status but would also reflect the different perspectives of the individuals, so the same item could have very different purposes. For example, a gorilla (as you will see in Part 2 of this block) could be one person's meat but another person's endangered species.

This diversity of perspectives is important when considering another of the recurring themes in this block: stakeholders. A ***stakeholder*** is any individual (or group of people) who has an interest in a particular issue, event, situation or project. Stakeholders may be directly or indirectly involved; they may have influence over a situation or simply feel the effects; their interest may be personal, commercial, emotional, financial, political … there are many possibilities. This is where conflict and cooperation come in. If the stakeholders have conflicting interests, perhaps over a shared resource, then cooperation in the form of recognising and accommodating these different stakeholder positions will be necessary if the conflict is to be resolved amicably.

River basin: the total area of land that is drained by a river and all its tributaries including the smallest streams. It is also sometimes known as the catchment or catchment area.

The title of this block refers to the Nile, but the geographical area of interest extends beyond the river alone and includes the entire Nile river basin. The Nile basin, like much of Africa, has a rising population and many people have limited access to water. Part 1 of this block will focus on water and the use of water as a resource. It will consider the multiple uses of water and their environmental and social impacts. Communities in Ethiopia will be highlighted to illustrate the problems and solutions associated with access to water for domestic and agricultural use.

Part 2 will look at an iconic species, the mountain gorilla, in the south-west of Uganda at the periphery of the Nile basin. It focuses on the conflicts between the desire to conserve them and the needs of the local people to use the resources of the forest where the gorillas live. The local people traditionally meet some of their livelihood needs by exploiting resources from the forest, but such exploitation can damage the gorilla habitat and their well-being. Part 2 considers the gorillas' need of the forest alongside the local people's needs from the forest. It seeks to understand how their conflicting interests have been negotiated, which has led to a cooperative approach to forest management. Thus, like Part 1, it also focuses on conflict and cooperation but in one specific corner of the Nile basin. It also builds on the theme of stakeholders and their different perspectives so there is much continuity with Part 1, although rather than looking at water resources, Part 2 looks at wildlife.

There are several extended activities in this block that are computer based. You will need to use your computer and the course DVD and, for one activity, you need to be online. As in previous blocks, this is indicated in this block by the DVD and/or online computer margin icons but so you know what to expect, these activities appear in Part 1 Sections 1, 4 and 5. In Part 2, Sections 1 and 2 are in text and the remainder is on the DVD, except the final summary, for which you should return to this book.

Part 1

Waters of the Nile

Pamela Furniss

Introduction 1

Finding the source of the River Nile was one of the great quests of British explorers in the nineteenth century. Speke, Burton, Grant, Livingstone and others made several pioneering expeditions into the 'interior' of the African continent in search of their goal. In 1862, John Hanning Speke claimed to have succeeded when he found the place on the north side of Lake Victoria where a huge river flows out of the lake (Figure 1.1).

(a) (b) (c)

Figure 1.1 The 'source' of the Nile: (a) In 1862, Speke (actually John Hanning, not John Hannington) claimed to have found the source of the Nile where the river flows out of Lake Victoria, near the town of Jinja, Uganda; (b) View from the same point, looking north from the 'source' in the direction of river flow; (c) On Lake Tana, Ethiopia at the outlet of the Abbay or Blue Nile. Traditional *tankwa* boats, made from papyrus, are still used today for fishing and transport.

In fact he had not got it quite right. The sources of the Nile are actually high in the mountains of Burundi, Rwanda and Kenya where the rivers that feed *into* Lake Victoria originate. These are the beginnings of the White Nile, so named because the water is coloured by the whitish clay particles suspended in it. The other main tributary, the Blue Nile, has its origins in the eastern African highlands in Ethiopia with the rivers that flow into Lake Tana. The river that leaves the lake, called the Abbay in Ethiopia, is known as the Blue Nile although in fact its colour is more usually brown because of the sediment it carries when in flood. These two great rivers meet at Khartoum in Sudan and flow northwards through Egypt to the Mediterranean (Figures 1.2 and 1.3).

The Nile flows predominantly from south to north over a great distance. As it does so it passes through many different climate and vegetation zones from forest, through grassland and the enormous expanse of the Sahara desert, to the coast. An important characteristic of the river is the huge seasonal variation in flow caused by the torrential rains that fall in the Ethiopian highlands. These feed the Blue Nile in summer, but in winter there is almost no rain and the river reduces to barely a trickle. The flow in the lower Nile, north of Khartoum, is sustained through the year by the more regular rainfall that feeds the White Nile and maintains a steady flow throughout the seasons. This combination of seasonal flooding on top of steady year-round flow is what made settlement and agriculture in the lower Nile valley possible. The waters of the Nile have provided the essential life-support system for human development and civilisation in this region for thousands of years, from the Ancient Egyptians to the present day.

This seasonal flow pattern is not always consistent. Sometimes the rains don't come. The Nile basin is a region known for its unreliable climate and occasional drought, with consequent disastrous impact on human life and the environment. Few who saw the television news of the time can forget the images of the Ethiopian famine in 1984 that prompted the Live Aid concerts and other relief campaigns. Water, essential to us all, is right at the heart of existence in this part of the world, and the impact of environmental change and uncertainty is severely felt.

This first part of Block 3 will describe the many ways in which people use water and will introduce some of the factors that influence water supply and availability, using examples from the Nile basin. It also aims to explore ways in which water can be used sustainably – or sometimes is not – in situations of shared use and limited supply.

Firstly, to set the scene for the later sections, there are two activities on the course DVD. The first is about exploring the Nile basin and the second asks you to compare water use in Ethiopia with your own.

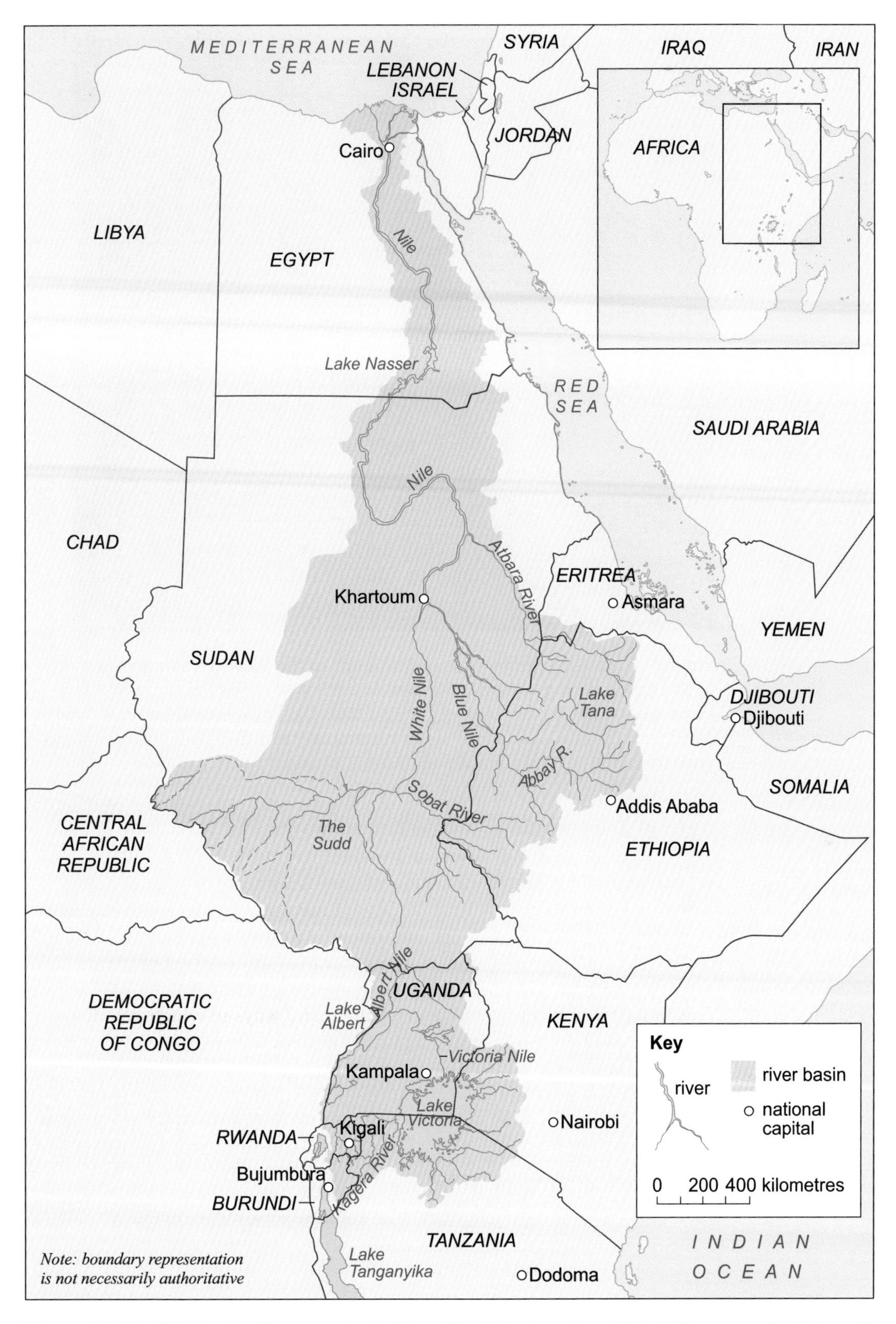

Figure 1.2 The Nile basin *(Source: adapted from World Bank, n.d. and World Resources Institute n.d.)*

Figure 1.3 Satellite photo of the confluence of the Blue and White Nile rivers at Khartoum during a flood. This false colour image shows the city of Khartoum at the lower right. The dark line is the Blue Nile. The White Nile, showing its 'white' colour in comparison, joins from lower left. Flooded farmland along the river banks appears dark blue. The surrounding desert is coloured pink.

For Activity 1.1 it is anticipated that you spend no more than 2 hours at your computer. Activity 1.2 starts on the course DVD with a video sequence and then asks you to take some measurements of your own water consumption. It is up to you to decide when you do this and it is obviously difficult to predict how long this may take but you are asked to assess your water use for a minimum of one day. You return to your computer to record your results and complete the activity. The computer-based part of Activity 1.2 should take no more than approximately 1 hour.

Activity 1.1 Exploring the Nile basin

On the course DVD, go to Block 3, Part 1 and click on 'Exploring the Nile basin'.

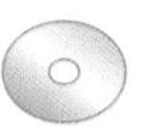

Activity 1.2 Water at home

On the course DVD, go to Block 3, Part 1 and click on 'Water at home'.

Whose water is it? 2

In the UK, the river basins are relatively small and the notion of international water ownership has limited relevance. But many rivers of the world, including the Nile, as you have seen in Activity 1.1, pass through a number of countries as they flow from source to mouth, and this inevitably leads to competition for the water resources.

SAQ 1.1 Countries of the Nile

Which three countries occupy the largest proportion of land area of the Nile basin? In general terms, what is the main difference in the amount of rainfall received in the north and the south of the basin area?

In many parts of the world, ownership of river water is determined by ownership of the river banks. These riparian owners (Latin: *ripa* = bank) claim ownership of the water that flows through their land. However, this arrangement fails to acknowledge that the water in a river is moving. If the river course crosses a boundary, whether between neighbouring gardens or international borders, the question arises: 'whose water is it?'

The riparian owners of an upstream section (nearer the source) may wish to take water from the river, thereby reducing the *quantity* that is available further downstream (nearer the mouth). They may pollute the water in some way, for example by discharging waste water from domestic or industrial premises, and thereby affect the *quality*. In any event, the activities of *upstream* water users will affect the potential activities of *downstream* users (Figure 1.4). It is easy to see that this could be a source of tension between upstream and downstream owners and that to avoid conflict, some sort of cooperation and agreement to share the water would be needed.

Figure 1.4 Upstream and downstream: the upstream users usually have the upper hand in terms of both (a) quantity and (b) quality

Even in a situation with only two parties to consider, some sort of negotiation between upstream and downstream owners would be required to establish an agreement on shared use, but the Nile has ten riparian countries to take into account. The White Nile flows through Uganda, Sudan and Egypt and the Blue Nile through Ethiopia, while Rwanda, Burundi, Democratic Republic of Congo, Kenya, Tanzania and Eritrea all have tributaries that flow into the Nile or Lake Victoria. Gaining agreement between so many stakeholders is inevitably challenging, but before looking at the current state of international agreements on the Nile it is necessary to go back in history a little because there are past agreements that still hold sway.

During the first half of the twentieth century Britain had political influence over approximately three-quarters of the Nile basin. The British approach was that securing a flow of water to Egypt, and to a lesser extent Sudan, was the priority (Howell and Allan, 1994, p. 5). The upstream countries, although most were also under British control, were not considered so important.

The Nile Waters Agreement of 1929, made between the Egyptian government and the British High Commissioner representing Sudan, gave Egypt the right to use almost all the Nile's water, apart from a tiny allocation to Sudan. The figures, based on contemporary estimates of flow, were 48 km^3 (cubic kilometres) annually to Egypt, 4 km^3 to Sudan and the remaining 32 km^3 to flow to the sea. (If you have trouble visualising very large volumes like this, try thinking of them as a cube. The 48 km^3 per year allocated to Egypt is equivalent to a cube with equal sides of very roughly 3.5 km, or more than 2 miles each – a lot of water!) The East African upstream countries were effectively forbidden from using the Nile waters at all. It is no surprise to learn that these countries were not signatories to this agreement – they were not involved in any way. The 1929 agreement said:

> Save with the previous agreement of the Egyptian Government, no irrigation or power works are to be constructed or taken on the River Nile or its branches, or on the lakes from which it flows so far as these are in the Sudan or in countries under British administration, which would, in such a manner as to entail any prejudice to the interests of Egypt, either reduce the quantity of water arriving in Egypt, or modify the date of its arrival, or lower its level.
>
> *(quoted in Howell and Allan, 1994, p. 85)*

In other words, Egypt was allowed complete control over any potential use of the Nile waters by the upstream countries. Although subsequently objected to by the countries of the upper Nile, this agreement has never been revoked so *theoretically* Egypt still 'owns' the water that flows out of Lake Victoria or Lake Tana and can veto its use by any upstream country.

This dominance of downstream riparian ownership is counter to the natural logic that you might expect. As suggested in Figure 1.4, power over the use of river water usually lies with the upstream owners simply because they get it first. They are usually in a position to dictate terms to the downstream user.

Why is the Nile basin situation different? (Part of the answer to this question was included in the DVD activity: 'Exploring the Nile basin'.) Egypt is, and always has been, totally dependent on the waters of the River Nile because of its climate – 86% of the country is classed as very arid (Kagwanja, 2007). Most of the population of Egypt, all of its major cities and all the cultural and historical sites of Ancient Egypt are in the Nile valley. As a consequence of this dependency, continued rights to use the water of the Nile have always been of the utmost importance. Egypt has always been vulnerable to any reduction in flow and so has vigorously opposed any upstream development plans. Sudan and parts of Ethiopia are also highly dependent on the Nile, but the other upstream countries less so because they have much higher annual rainfall. But the main reason for the continued dominance of Egypt is its greater political, military and economic power. This, combined with internal conflict and poverty in several of the upstream countries in the latter part of the twentieth century, allowed the unequal rights to the water to continue (Timmerman, 2005).

In 1959, the Nile Waters Treaty, agreed between Egypt and Sudan only, gave Sudan a slightly larger allocation than before. One significant advance was improvement to data collection methods that enabled the 1959 treaty to be based on more accurate measurements of water flow. The treaty increased Sudan's share to approximately a third that of Egypt's, and together they accounted for 84% of the total river flow. Again, the upstream countries had no rights to the water at all, but by this time, objections were growing.

> In the early 1960s Julius Nyerere, then the leader of independent Tanganyika (not yet Tanzania), declared that 'former colonial countries had no role in the formulation and conclusion of treaties done during the colonial era, and therefore they must not be assumed to automatically succeed to those treaties'. Nyerere bluntly told Britain and the other Nile countries that he had no intention of adhering to the 1929 Nile agreement. Kenya and Uganda agreed with Nyerere. Egypt – which benefited most from the now rejected agreement – did not, but there was nothing it could do about it.
>
> *(de Villiers, 1999)*

Egypt was prepared to defend its claims on the river, however. In 1970 Ethiopia proposed a dam near Lake Tana to preserve some of the Blue Nile headwaters for itself. Egyptian president Anwar Sadat threatened war. Again, in 1978, President Sadat said 'we depend upon the Nile 100 percent in our life, so if anyone, at any moment thinks to deprive us of our life we shall never hesitate [to go to war] because it is a matter of life or death' (Waterbury, 1979, p. 78).

Although there was no war, Egypt used other means to protect its interests by covert destabilisation of the upstream countries (Kagwanja, 2007). For example, at various times Egypt gave financial and military support to Eritreans fighting against the Ethiopian government and also to the Somalis fighting against Kenya. As noted above, internal unrest in Ethiopia and the other upstream countries, coupled with lack of funds, prevented their plans for major water projects from coming to fruition. Egypt also used its power to influence the availability of financial assistance for water projects. For example, in 1988 when Ethiopia began a water management project on Lake Tana, Egypt blocked a loan for the project from the African Development Bank (Kagwanja, 2007).

In the 1990s, the situation began to change. The need for cooperation was recognised and the Technical Cooperation Committee for the Promotion of Development and Environmental Protection of the Nile Basin (known as Tecconile) was established. This was the first collaborative group of Nile stakeholders, with six of the riparian countries as members and the other four as observers. The underlying principle was voiced by the Prime Minister of Ethiopia, who said:

> What we basically need is to deal with the Nile basin as a single region with shared natural resources. If we take this as a basis for dealing with the Nile issue, we will be able to devise better ways to achieve the maximum benefit from its waters.
>
> *(Meles Zenawi, Prime Minister of Ethiopia (and Open University MBA), 7 April 1998, quoted in Collins, 2003)*

In 1999 Tecconile was replaced by the Nile Basin Initiative (NBI), which had nine of the ten Nile basin countries as active members (all except Eritrea). It was intended to be 'a unique forum for the countries of the Nile to move forward a cooperative process to realize tangible benefits in the Basin and build a solid foundation of trust and confidence' (Metawie, 2004). The primary objectives of the NBI were:

- to develop the Nile Basin water resources in a sustainable and equitable way to ensure prosperity, security and peace for all its peoples
- to ensure efficient water management and the optimal use of the resources
- to ensure cooperation and joint action between the riparian countries, seeking win–win gains
- to target poverty eradication and promote economic integration
- to ensure that the program results in a move from planning to action.

(NBI, 2009)

These are admirable aims but they are challenging and unlikely to be achieved quickly. A great deal of diplomatic debate and multinational negotiation is needed to review the historical claims and arrive at new agreements, although progress has been made. In 2003 and 2004, Kenya, Uganda and Tanzania all raised objections to the 1929 and 1959 treaties and to Egypt's dominance over the Nile waters. In response, Egypt adjusted its policy from confrontation to cooperation, although still resisting projects that would diminish the amount of water available. Egypt has since given grants to upstream countries for smaller projects that would not affect the volume of water reaching Egypt.

In April 2006, the NBI negotiations led to the formation of a permanent commission, the Nile River Basin Commission (NRBC) or sometimes just Nile Basin Commission (NBC). There is now therefore a forum for discussion among the Nile riparian states and an expectation that future water use can be shared equitably among them. However, the issue of the historical pacts on the Nile waters remains unresolved.

Peter Kagwanja sums up the situation:

> The Nile River Basin has witnessed a shift from antagonism to cooperation among riparian states in the utilization of resources. However, the lingering question is whether the radical shift in the Egyptian approach reflects a genuine change of heart or simply a strategic retreat as it ponders alternative ways of retaining its firm grip on the Nile. What is certain, though, is that regional structures now have the capacity to resolve disputes and work to avert any potential 'water wars'. This marks a triumph of regionalism over stateism, and multilateralism over unilateralism.
>
> *(Kagwanja, 2007, p. 333)*

Kagwanja's summary, despite his cautionary note about Egypt's intentions, brings out the importance of cooperation to resolve conflict, or at least attempts to resolve it, where there are many stakeholders. His last sentence reflects the need for any river catchment to be viewed as an integrated whole, not to be divided up along national borders, and that all stakeholders need to be considered, not just a single dominant player.

Study note: critical reading and possible bias

Whenever you are reading from books, articles, journals, websites, etc. you need to try to make a judgement on the reliability and possible bias of your source. This is especially true if you intend to quote from the source yourself, as I have done here. Just because something is in print, it doesn't necessarily mean it's true. Web pages in particular can vary enormously in reliability and should always be viewed critically.

The quote above is taken from an academic journal, which I consider to be a reasonably reliable source. I base this view on the knowledge that most academic journals use a process of '***peer review***', meaning that qualified academic reviewers who are knowledgeable in the subject are invited to read and comment on submitted articles before they are accepted for publication. But even though this provides some assurance of the objectivity of the article, it is worth bearing in mind that the writer's perspective will always be present. The author's opinion will almost certainly have influenced the words and emphasis they use. For example, it is possible that the comment about Egypt's change of heart in the quote above could be a reflection of the author's own political or national perspective rather than an entirely objective, unbiased view. I do not have any evidence to support that view – and, of course, I am revealing my own perspective in suggesting it – but it is a possibility worth keeping in mind.

Summary of Section 2

Control over the use of river waters usually lies with upstream riparian owners rather than downstream owners because they have access to the water first. In the Nile basin, treaties and agreements made in the twentieth century favoured Egypt and Sudan because of colonial and political factors, and gave them authority over the use of the Nile waters, to the disadvantage of the upstream countries. The Nile Basin Initiative and Nile Basin Commission, involving nine of the ten riparian countries, now provide a forum for negotiation over future water use that should lead to more equitable allocation of the resource.

Water – a renewable resource

The historical context described above is unique to the River Nile. Although there are shared international river basins elsewhere in the world, no others have quite the same complex history. However, there are other aspects of rivers and water use that are universal, and these will be the focus of this section. It is necessary to look beyond the river itself in order to appreciate the significance of water and its crucial role in our lives.

One very obvious feature of a river is that the water in it is moving. If you were asked to give a definition of a river, the first thing you might say is 'flowing water' or, perhaps a little more precisely, 'water moving downhill in a channel'. This movement of river water is an essential part of a much larger dynamic system – the ***water cycle*** or ***hydrological cycle*** – that sustains our entire existence and that of all life on earth.

3.1 The water cycle

Water on the Earth's surface moves in an unceasing cycle through rivers, oceans, clouds and rain. The cycle requires energy to keep it turning and this is provided by the Sun. The Sun's heat causes evaporation of water, principally from the oceans. The water vapour it produces is moved around by winds and may condense into clouds. Rain and snow, collectively known as precipitation, fall from the clouds. The water runs off the land and collects into streams and rivers, which flow down to the sea and complete the cycle. This very simplified description of the water cycle is shown in a little more detail in Figure 1.5.

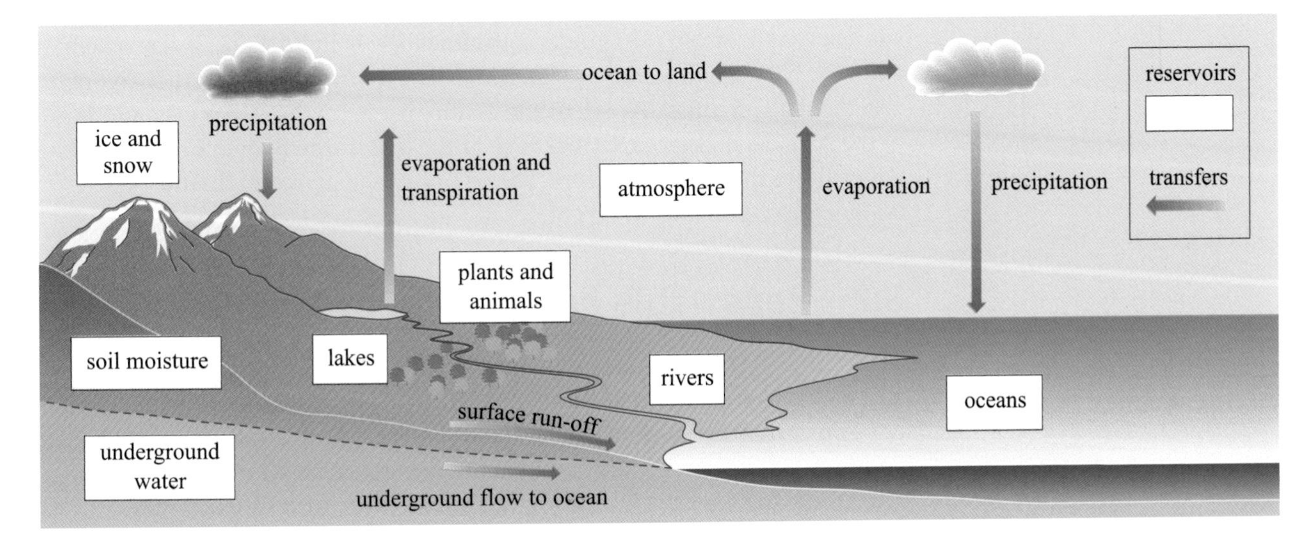

Figure 1.5 The water cycle

Other contributions to this basic outline of the cycle have been included in Figure 1.5. As well as evaporating from the oceans, water also evaporates from lakes, rivers, marshes and other freshwater sources into the atmosphere. In addition it evaporates from the soil and from the surface of the leaves of plants. Plants draw water up through their roots to the leaves, from where some evaporates into the atmosphere in the process of ***transpiration***. These combined processes of water loss are known as ***evapotranspiration***.

About three times as much rain falls on the ocean as on the land. Of the water that does fall on land, some of it will soak (infiltrate) into the ground rather than running off the surface into rivers. Depending on geological conditions, the infiltrating water may become part of the reservoir of ***groundwater*** which can be found in some permeable rocks. Water, and other liquids such as oil, can pass into and through permeable rocks (as opposed to impermeable rocks) in tiny spaces within their structure. Underground rock strata that hold water are called ***aquifers***. This water may move under gravitational influence, thus contributing to the cycling process by flowing underground through the rocks.

Our need for water, and that of other land animals and plants, is met by tapping into the water cycle at some point between precipitation on to land and discharge back to the sea. Almost all our water is abstracted from rivers, lakes or aquifers and we rely on the processes of the water cycle to constantly replenish and renew our supply.

One component of the water cycle that varies depending on where you are in the world is evaporation, which is directly related to temperature. The Nile catchment differs from most other river systems in the rest of the world in that much of the river flows through a vast, hot desert. Most rivers get larger from source to mouth in terms of the volume of water flowing in them because of the tributaries joining the main channel. The Nile is unusual in that the volume of water actually decreases. The only major tributary, apart from the Blue and White Niles, is the Atbara River, which joins the Nile roughly halfway down its length. After that no other rivers join the main channel. North of the confluence with the Atbara the volume of the Nile decreases, partly because of the losses due to evaporation as the water flows through the desert. This is one of the reasons why the Nile waters are so precious to Egypt.

3.2 Renewable and non-renewable resources

The introduction to this block included a brief explanation of resources and mentioned possible groupings such as physical, biological and environmental. An alternative and widely used categorisation is renewable and non-renewable resources. The basic difference between the two is the rate at which they are renewed or regenerated back into a usable form, relative to the rate at which they are used by humans.

Renewable resources can be regenerated over short, or relatively short, timescales. In some cases, the regeneration of the resource results from the functioning of some natural system – water is a prime example of this; solar and wave energy are others. Other types of renewable resource are regenerated through processes involving the growth of plants or animals. These have increasingly become managed by humans, most obviously in agriculture and forestry. In some cases, renewable resources are available more or less continuously, for example annually grown crops. In others, the regeneration periods may be longer – 15 to 20 years for some commercial softwoods like pine, and longer still, up to 200 or 300 years, in the case of some types of hardwood such as oak.

Non-renewable resources, like coal, are different. Coal is formed by the decomposition of plant material, but the full cycle of transition from the deposition of vegetation to the formation of hard coal would take many millions of years. An argument could be made that, in theory, non-renewable resources are, in fact, renewable – but the crucial difference is that this would not be on human timescales. Whereas the timescales for renewable resources are of the order of human lifetimes, the time required to produce non-renewable resources is very, very long indeed. If you think back to the discussion of geological timescales and deep time in Block 1, you will appreciate that the time required would be so enormous that effectively they are not renewable.

Activity 1.3 Renewable and non-renewable resources

Which of these are renewable resources and which are non-renewable, and why?

Oil, wind, copper, forest, water.

Discussion

Oil, a fossil fuel, is a classic example of a non-renewable resource. Like coal, it took millions of years of the Earth's development to create the oil deposits that we now exploit and although, theoretically, the same geological processes could repeat, this would take several more millions of years. In effect, there is a finite amount and ultimately it will be used up.

Wind, as a source of energy, is in constant supply and does not get used up, so is a classic renewable resource.

Copper, extracted from copper ore, is also the product of processes over geological timescales and so is non-renewable. It differs from oil, however, in that it is not burned or transformed when used and so can often be re-used or recycled.

Forest is renewable in the sense that if trees are cut down then new trees can be grown to replace them, assuming that conditions remain suitable. But there is obviously a time period of several decades required for this new growth to take place – so it is renewable but not instantly. There are other considerations here too, because this renewability considers 'forest' only as trees and the wood derived from them. If you think of forest as an entire ecosystem supporting many different plants and animals, and of its possible aesthetic value, then its renewability may be questionable. In addition, the rich diversity of species in a long-established forest of mixed, native trees would not be recreated if they were cut and replaced by a plantation of a single introduced tree type, grown for commercial value.

Water, as shown by the water cycle, is a renewable resource that circulates around the Earth and is constantly replenished. But there are some limitations to this renewability, discussed later.

This discussion suggests that a straightforward two-way classification into renewable and non-renewable resources may be an oversimplification. The boundaries are indistinct – copper is non-renewable but not in the same way as oil; forest is renewable up to a point, and in some ways but not in others. In practice it can be more useful to think of resources as a continuum depending on their recyclability and the consequences that may follow from their use by humans (Figure 1.6).

type	renewability		example
renewable resources	less susceptible to human modification	high ↑	solar energy water power
	more susceptible to human modification		soil forest
non-renewable resources	more recyclable		metals
	less recyclable not recyclable	↓ low	fossil fuels

Figure 1.6 Types of environmental resource *(Source: adapted from Mather and Chapman, 1995)*

SAQ 1.2 Are fish renewable?

Looking at Figure 1.6, where would you put 'fish' (in the sense of fish stocks) in the list of examples on the right-hand side?

For non-renewable resources such as oil or copper, another important concept is ***reserves***. Reserves of a particular resource are those parts of it which:

(a) have been proven to exist, for example by exploratory drilling, and

(b) can be recovered by mining or some other method of extraction.

Even when a resource is recoverable, it may not make sense to extract it, for instance because the reserve is small, is of poor quality, or is too deep below the surface of the Earth. In such cases, extraction would be too expensive relative to the potential profit and so not economically sensible. Consequently, there is a further distinction between reserves and ***usable reserves***, that is, the reserves that are economically and technically available for extraction.

The size of usable reserve for any resource is not a fixed amount. Exploration leading to further discoveries, technological improvements in extraction techniques and, importantly, the changing economic value of the end product will all influence the size of the usable reserve. For example, some oilfields in the North Sea that were previously considered to be exhausted have become viable again because of new technology, including better drilling techniques, in combination with increased oil prices. Similarly, new sources that may have been known about for some time may become usable reserves if the price of the ultimate product increases.

This brief diversion into reserves of non-renewable resources may seem a distraction from the discussion about water which, as noted above, is a renewable resource. However, in some circumstances, water is not renewable. In the normal functioning of the water cycle, aquifers are recharged by rain and snow falling on land and the water infiltrating into permeable rock below. In some circumstances, geological changes may lead to aquifers being sealed by impermeable rock layers so they cease to be recharged. The water remains 'locked' in the sealed aquifer and is effectively removed from the water cycle and therefore becomes a non-renewable resource. These deposits, referred to as *fossil water*, have remained in place for millions of years and extraction from these reserves is known as *water mining*. The world's largest fossil water system is the Nubian Sandstone Aquifer System (NSAS). It extends over an area of more than 2 million km^2 in North Africa beneath Egypt, Sudan, Libya and Chad and is an extremely important potential water resource in this region. It is estimated to hold more than 500 000 km^3 of water, of which approximately 15 000 km^3 is considered recoverable (IAEA, 2007). Libya, Sudan and Egypt are using the aquifer to supply fresh water to their main cities and are currently extracting fossil water from the aquifer at a rate of approximately 6.5 million m^3 per day.

Study note: conversion of units

The paragraph above refers to volumes of water using two different units – km^3 (cubic kilometres) and m^3 (cubic metres). To perform calculations using data like these, as you are asked to do in the following SAQ, you need to convert them so that only one unit is used. If not expressed using the same units, any answer you get will be nonsense. For example, imagine you are calculating the size of a carpet needed for a room that measures 3 metres by 4 metres, which could also be measured as 300 centimetres by 400 centimetres. The area, of course, is 12 m^2 but if you mistakenly calculated 3×400 you would get 1200 with a strange unit equivalent to 'metres times centimetres'.

To convert units from one form to another, you need to know the relationship between them; in this case, how many m^3 there are in a km^3. You may want to look back to Box 2.3 in Block 1 for a list of SI prefixes and their names. The Study note on powers of ten in Block 2 may also be useful.

Here are a few example conversions.

For linear measurements:

$$1\ \text{km} = 1000\ \text{m}$$

which can also be written as:

$$1\ \text{km} = 1 \times 10^{3}\ \text{m}$$

and, to convert from m to km

$$1\ \text{m} = 0.001\ \text{km}$$

which can also be written as:

$$1\ \text{m} = 1 \times 10^{-3}\ \text{km}$$

For measurement of area:

$$\begin{aligned} 1\ \text{km}^2 &= 1000\ \text{m} \times 1000\ \text{m} \\ &= 1\,000\,000\ \text{m}^2 \end{aligned}$$

which can also be written as:

$$1\ \text{km}^2 = 1 \times 10^{6}\ \text{m}^2$$

and, to convert from m^2 to km^2

$$\begin{aligned} 1\ \text{m}^2 &= 0.000001 \text{ or} \\ &= 1 \times 10^{-6}\ \text{km}^2 \end{aligned}$$

For measurement of volume:

$$\begin{aligned} 1\ \text{km}^3 &= 1000\ \text{m} \times 1000\ \text{m} \times 1000\ \text{m} \\ &= 1\,000\,000\,000\ \text{m}^3 \end{aligned}$$

which can also be written as:

$$1\ \text{km}^3 = 1 \times 10^{9}\ \text{m}^3$$

and, to convert from m^3 to km^3

$$1\ \text{m}^3 = 1 \times 10^{-9}\ \text{km}^3$$

SAQ 1.3 Using fossil water

Assuming there are no other extractions from the NSAS, how long will the reserve last if water continues to be removed at the rate given above?

Would you describe this as sustainable use?

One question that arises over use of any aquifer is who owns it. The NSAS extends beneath four countries and, of course, its boundaries do not correspond to the national borders at the surface. Conventionally, landowners, including nation states, claim ownership of all mineral and other resources that lie under their land. As water is pumped out of the aquifer from wells it will very slowly be replaced by water that is drawn in from the surrounding permeable rock. (Imagine sucking water out of a sponge through a straw.) Ultimately this water may have originated in rocks that lie beneath a different country. The potential for conflict over underground water resources, where the origin of the water and the exact extent of the aquifer may not be known, is clear to see.

3.3 Water quality

There is another aspect of the renewability of water to consider. When humans extract water from a river for use in some way, it follows that after they have used it, they need to get rid of it. The most obvious and easiest means for disposal is often to put it back in the river. But the water is almost certain to have been changed in some way. Depending on what the water was used for, it may contain a whole variety of pollutants, many of which are likely to be ***organic matter*** of some sort. This may be from human wastes, animal wastes, agriculture, some industrial processes and other sources. Fortunately for us, given the right conditions, water is able to cleanse itself of many pollutants by physical processes (such as deposition, dispersal and dilution – see Box 1.1) and by the action of micro-organisms on organic matter. So not only is the quantity maintained by the action of the water cycle, but also the quality can be renewed by these natural processes.

Box 1.1 Water pollution

In Block 2 you were introduced to the idea that a pollutant can be any substance that has adverse effects on the environment. Water pollutants can include a wide variety of substances including organic matter, inert (i.e. unreactive) solids like sand and silt, pathogens (that cause disease), toxic chemicals including ***heavy metals***, persistent organic pollutants (POPs), and others. All of these substances may find their way into a watercourse or water body and potentially cause harm to the wildlife and people that use the water.

Once released into the environment, there are several possible processes that may ameliorate the effects of a pollutant. Organic matter may be removed by biological processes as it is broken down by micro-organisms. In addition there are physical processes such as ***deposition***, ***dispersal*** and ***dilution*** that all contribute to reducing the impact of water pollutants.

Solid material may settle out (be *deposited*) at the bottom of a water body and become part of the accumulating sediment, or it may be *dispersed* in the flow of moving water and spread out so widely that its effects are greatly reduced. Substances that dissolve in the water may be greatly *diluted* by large water volumes such that the amount present in any fixed volume is very small. In situations where the volumes of water are large enough, dispersal and dilution may mean that the pollutant ceases to be a problem. (The exceptions to this are those pollutants that are accumulated within the bodies of animals that consume the water, e.g. POPs and heavy metals. These continue to be a problem even at very low concentrations.)

However, there are limits to the capacity of any river to cleanse itself in this way. The removal of organic matter depends on certain bacteria, and some other microscopic organisms, which use the organic matter as food. In order to get energy from the organic matter, the micro-organisms break down some of it in the process of respiration, which needs oxygen.

SAQ 1.4 Respiration

Describe the process of respiration in terms of its starting materials and products. (You may want to refer back to Block 1 Part 2.)

If large quantities of organic matter are discharged into a river, the population of micro-organisms increases in response and will take more and more oxygen out of the water. If the inputs of organic material are high, oxygen is removed from the water faster than it can re-enter from the atmosphere. This can lead to complete ***deoxygenation*** of the water, with consequent death of fish and other aquatic animals that depend for their survival on there being adequate oxygen dissolved in the water.

In the UK and many other parts of the world, most used water goes via sewers to sewage treatment works. Treatment processes usually include a biological stage in which organic material is broken down by micro-organisms, in much the same way as it would be in a river. Sewage treatment works are designed to provide adequate oxygen to enable this breakdown of organic matter by micro-organisms to take place (Figure 1.7).

(a) (b)

Figure 1.7 Sewage treatment works: (a) Aeration tanks. Oxygen is provided by forced aeration using air pumps or physical aerators; the population of micro-organisms lives in the mixed liquid, called activated sludge; **(b) Trickling filters.** Sewage is trickled over a wide area of filter material (usually lumps of rock) which provides a large surface area on which the micro-organisms grow. The air spaces between the lumps of rock allow close contact between micro-organisms, sewage and oxygen.

By the time the effluent is discharged into a river, following biological treatment and settlement, the organic content should be almost nil (assuming that the sewage works is functioning properly). In places where there is minimal or no sewage treatment, or no sewers, then used water will pass directly into rivers or ditches. In a large river the volume of flow may be sufficient to adequately dilute the incoming effluent, but in many instances the river or stream will be unable to cope with the organic load. This may lead to stretches of deoxygenated water unable to support aquatic life and, at worst, can result in stinking, open sewers running through towns and cities (Figure 1.8). Although not so obvious, groundwater may also be contaminated by sewage, or other liquid pollutants, infiltrating from the surface.

Figure 1.8 Open sewer: sewage and other waste water, rain and solid waste all collect in the same channel through a residential area

Human waste is not only a source of organic matter in rivers but also potentially of several diseases, which are discussed in the next section. There are two other major sources of water pollution – industry and agriculture. Industrial effluents are highly varied depending on the processes involved. They may include dissolved metallic compounds and many other chemicals that may be highly toxic to the environment. Run-off from agricultural land can include excess fertilisers and also pesticides. Fertilisers are designed to provide nutrients for crops, but in the aquatic environment they can lead to excessive growth of algae and other plants. These can choke the water flow, and when the plants die, the decay of their residues can deoxygenate the water. In the Nile basin, water hyacinth is a particular problem (see Box 1.2).

Box 1.2 Water hyacinth

Water hyacinth is a free-floating water plant, a native of South America that has spread throughout many parts of the world. In Africa, North America and Asia it has become a significant problem and is a classic example of an invasive exotic (non-native) species. It grows extremely fast and can rapidly spread across extensive areas of water. It is a major problem in Lake Victoria, where the climate is suitable and it lacks natural enemies.

Figure 1.9 Water hyacinth

The problems it causes include clogging of waterways so boats cannot pass through, and clogging of intake works for water supply or hydroelectric power plants. It interferes with fishing activities, blocks out sunlight and air from the water surface to the detriment of aquatic life, and deoxygenates the water when it dies back. Controlling water hyacinth becomes a continual necessity and creates a significant economic burden.

Water quality can also be affected by the presence of particulate material carried along suspended in flowing water. Large quantities of these suspended solids, typically inert particles of sand, silt and mud, will greatly increase the ***turbidity*** of the water. This can prevent sunlight from penetrating below the water surface and therefore affect the growth of water plants. It can also affect fish and other animals that feed on small particles of food in the water. If the speed of water flow reduces, for example where a river flows into a lake or reservoir, then the solids will settle out into layers of sediment at the bottom. In large quantities the solids may smother aquatic organisms and their habitat.

The particulate material comes from soil and rock that is washed off the land into rivers by rain. Soil erosion is a significant problem in many parts of the Nile basin (Figure 1.10). The quantity of solid material will be influenced by several factors including the intensity of rainfall, the slope of the land, and the presence and type of vegetation. Heavy rain, bare soils and steep slopes will all contribute to larger quantities of solid material being washed into rivers.

Figure 1.10 Soil erosion in Ethiopia. Deep gulleys have formed where rain has washed away the soil in places with little vegetation cover. As an indication of scale, notice the small group of people to the left of the two trees.

3.4 Water-borne disease

Sanitation: the prevention of human contact with wastes for hygienic purposes. Basic sanitation at household level means access to a toilet of some sort but the term can also be applied to provision of sewers, drainage and treatment systems.

Quite apart from the problems of organic pollution and its effects on the river ecosystem, a much more significant issue, in terms of human health, is the transmission of disease through contaminated water. If people do not have access to sanitation, i.e. toilets (Figures 1.11 and 1.12), they are forced to defecate in fields, ditches and buckets. In urban slums, the only option sometimes is to defecate into a plastic bag which is then thrown out on to the street. If sanitation is inadequate, then human waste can very easily get into rivers, ponds and groundwater. These same rivers, ponds and groundwater are often the source of water for many people. If the waste comes from people or animals infected with certain diseases, then the people using the water are likely to become infected themselves. This leads to a repeating cycle of infection from humans to water and then back to humans.

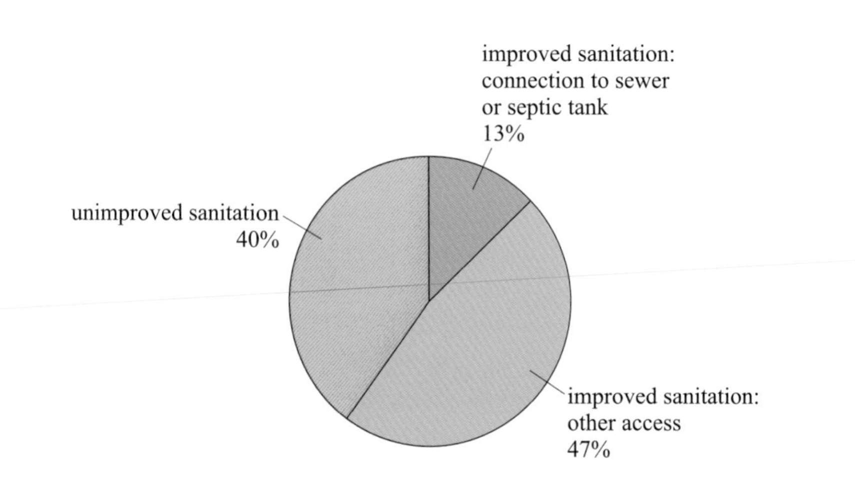

Figure 1.11 Sanitation in Africa: percentage of population by type of sanitation, 2000. Improved sanitation can mean a flush toilet connected to a septic tank or sewer system; it can also mean a pour-flush latrine or a pit latrine. Sanitation facilities are considered adequate if they are private or shared (but not public), and if they can effectively prevent direct contact between the faeces and people, animals and/or insects. *(Source: Clarke and King, 2004, p. 50)*

Cholera, typhoid, dysentery and polio are all transmitted by consumption of water polluted by human faecal material that contains the relevant bacterium or virus. Consumption may be directly by drinking from contaminated supplies or indirectly through poor hygiene in food preparation or personal washing. Diarrhoea, a symptom of many diseases, is often caused by a relatively simple intestinal infection. Left untreated, diarrhoea causes acute dehydration, which is one of the leading causes of death in children, especially malnourished children, in Africa and Asia. Worldwide, nearly 1 800 000 people died from diarrhoeal disease in the year 2002 (UNESCO, 2006).

(a)

(b)

Figure 1.12 (a) Pit latrine in rural Ethiopia. Simple pit latrines like this one are essentially just a hole in the ground, but they contain the waste in the pit beneath and keep it away from the surface; (b) In urban slums, plastic bags are used and then simply thrown out on to the streets where they accumulate in drainage channels and frequently split open.

Other water-borne diseases are caused by parasites, many of which have complicated life cycles. Some, like Guinea worm, are transmitted to humans who consume infected water, others merely by coming into contact with it. Schistosomiasis, also known as bilharzia, is a severely debilitating disease widespread in parts of Africa and also found in the Middle East, Asia and South America. It is caused by a parasitic flatworm that spends part of its life in a human host and partly in a particular species of water snail. The worms have a complicated life cycle that depends on a repeating sequence of events (Figure 1.13). The eggs of the worms can be found in lakes and rivers where these have been contaminated by excreta from infected humans. The eggs are eaten by the snails. They hatch inside and the larvae are excreted by the snail into the water, where they rest on the stems and leaves of aquatic plants. If people brush against the plants, the larvae penetrate through the skin and into the bloodstream. Once inside the human body they mature into adult worms and lodge in the intestines or bladder. Subsequently their eggs are passed out of the body in faeces or urine, can re-enter the watercourse and so complete the cycle. People living nearby use the water in many ways that bring them into contact with the plants and therefore the worms. Farmers and fishermen, women washing clothes, children playing, and anyone washing in the water are all at risk and very likely to be infected. Schistosomiasis rarely causes death but its effects include chronic fatigue and increased susceptibility to a wide range of other diseases. It is estimated that approximately 200 million people worldwide are infected.

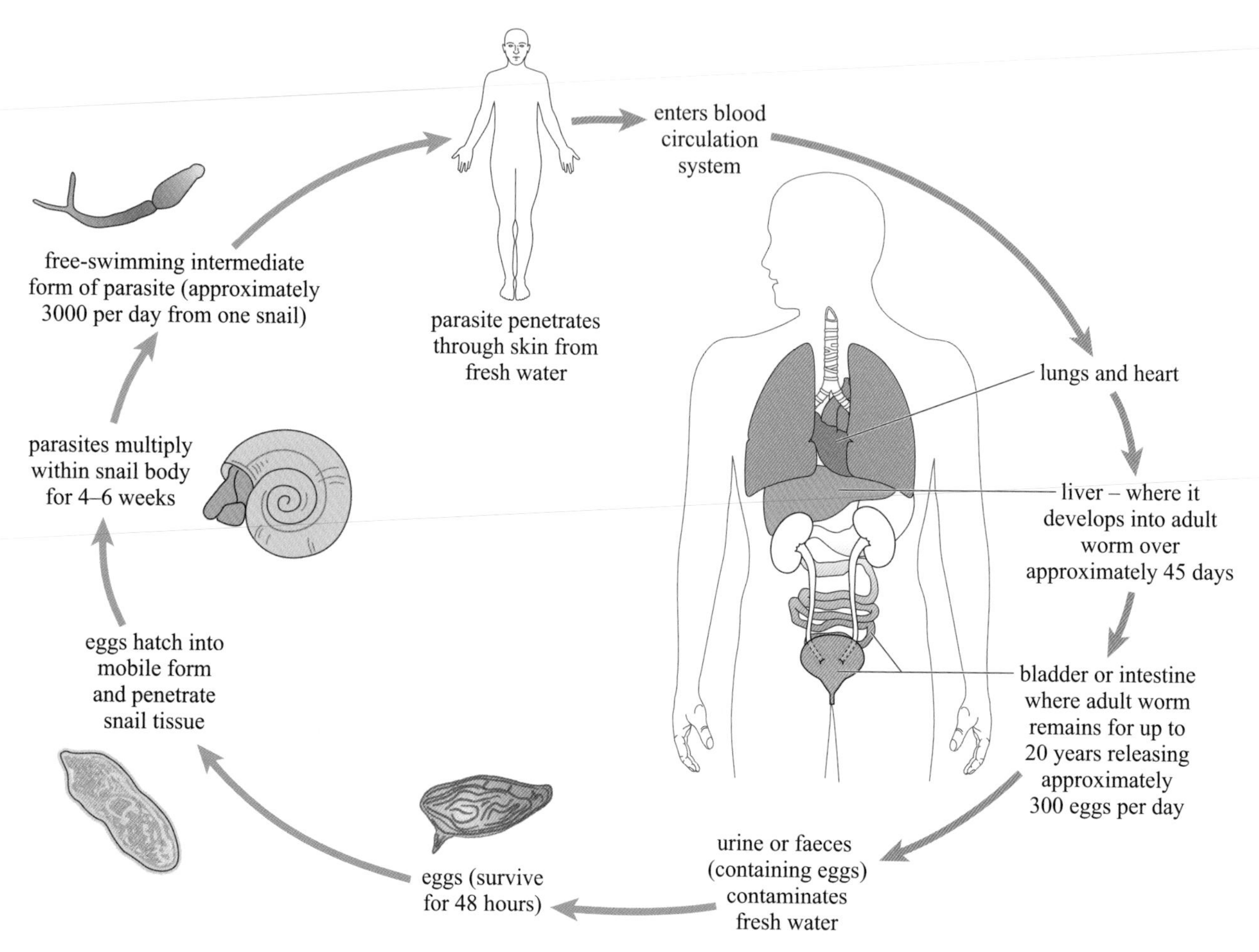

Figure 1.13 Schistosomiasis life cycle

Breaking the cycle of water-borne disease depends on either preventing human waste from reaching the water or preventing infected water from reaching humans. An adequate sanitation system that either treats the sewage or, at minimum, contains the waste so that it does not reach the water supply, is one approach. The other is to provide safe water supplies from uncontaminated sources. Ideally, both approaches are used. A third requirement is to ensure that people understand how the diseases are spread and the importance of hygiene, such as washing hands in clean water after going to the toilet, if that is possible for them.

SAQ 1.5 Ethiopian lives

Think back to the stories of the two women from Ethiopia you saw in Activity 1.2. Where did they get their water from? What are the potential sources of water pollution in both cases?

3.5 Water systems

System is a word familiar in phrases such as education system, transport system, heating system, blood circulation system. Earlier in this section I referred to the water cycle as a dynamic system and also mentioned river systems and the Nubian Aquifer System. But what does the word 'system' mean? Describing these things as systems suggests that there is a degree of complexity involved and that these are not single entities. For example, the blood circulation system consists of veins, arteries, heart, blood flow, pulse, etc.; the education system consists of schools, teachers, teaching approaches, learning styles, exams, curriculum, etc.; the water cycle system consists of many water reservoirs linked by water movement processes. (By reservoirs I mean not only surface water bodies but all parts of the cycle where water is held, i.e. clouds, oceans, rivers, groundwater, etc. – see Figure 1.5.) A ***system*** can be defined as a selected set of related components together with the connections between them. Identifying and thinking in terms of systems can be a helpful approach to understanding complex, interconnected situations.

An important aspect of defining any system is deciding what is part of the system and what is not: in other words, deciding on the system components and the system boundary. For example, when I refer to the Nile as a river system I mean the two main rivers, all the tributaries, lakes, etc. Other river systems could also be described in this way, that is, the system includes all the watercourses and connected water bodies of the catchment. When referring to the water cycle as a system, there are additional components and the boundary is considerably wider. It includes river systems and also the other water reservoirs (oceans, groundwater, atmosphere) as well as the transfer processes of the cycle (condensation, precipitation, evaporation, etc.). Figure 1.14 shows the water cycle in the form of a ***systems map***. The line around the outside is the boundary of the system and within it are the components. I have used the water cycle components from Figure 1.5, with some minor amendments to avoid repetition.

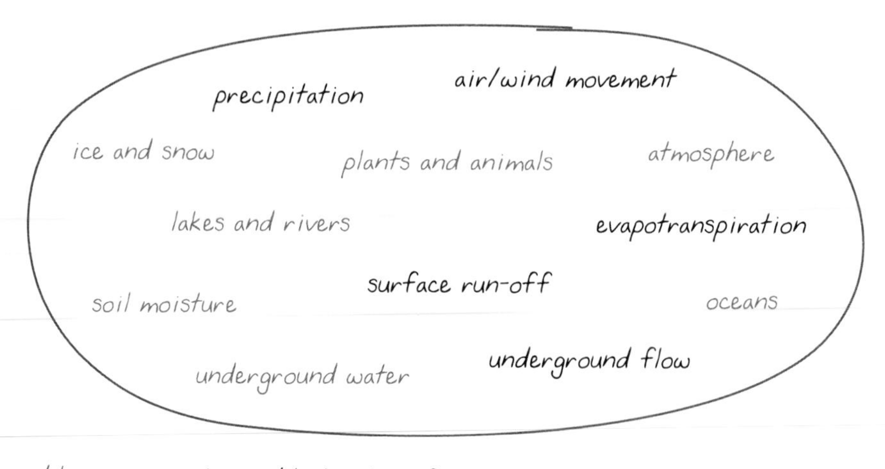

Figure 1.14 Water cycle system

An alternative title for Figure 1.14 might be a 'water resource system'. However, this does not include the effects of human activity so would be more accurately described as a *natural* water resource system. If you recall from the Introduction to Block 3, resources are defined by their use by humans, so a more complete description of a water resource system should include the human element within the system boundary (Figure 1.15).

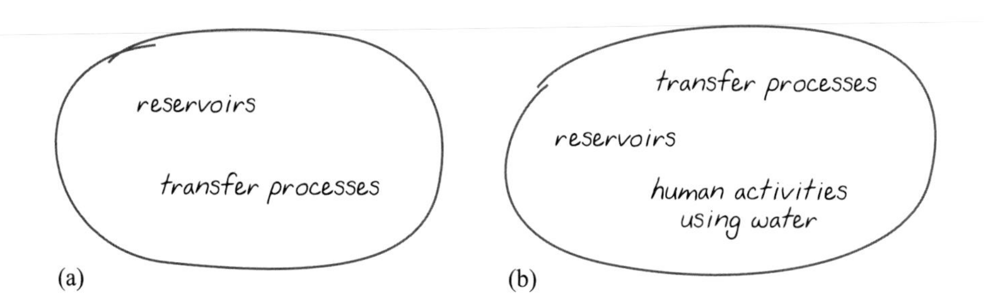

Figure 1.15 (a) Natural water resource system; (b) water resource system. Note that (a) is a simplified version of Figure 1.14; the components have been grouped as reservoirs and transfer processes.

This brings up an important point. It is possible to identify all sorts of different systems in the same situation. Although each system contains elements that exist in the physical world, what I choose to include or not include is my individual decision. Formally, systems in this sense are *constructs* and it means that you and I, or anyone else, may well identify very different systems in a particular situation. This links back to the definition of a system, given above, as 'a *selected* set of related components' – the system of interest depends on who is doing the selection. To use another example, think back to the discussion of Activity 1.3 and possible perspectives on a forest. A forester's view of a forest system may consist only of the trees. A naturalist, however, would define their system of interest differently and would be likely to include other plants, birds and other animals.

(You may notice that systems maps have some similarities with Venn diagrams, which were introduced in Block 1 Part 4. A Venn diagram shows the classification of objects into sets that share certain properties. The aim of a systems map is not to classify things but to show the structure and relationships of a system of interest. Venn diagrams are more objective because they show logical relationships, whereas systems maps are more subjective because the choice of system boundary and components can vary depending on the perspective of the person creating it.)

Though not made explicit in the diagram, there are many links between the human activities in Figure 1.15(b) and the reservoirs and processes of the water cycle. And the links work both ways: the activities affect and are affected by the natural system. This is made clear in this definition of a water resource system as:

> an integrated complex of interlinked hydrological and socio-economic variables operating together within a well-defined area, commonly a drainage-basin unit
>
> *(O'Riordan and More, 1969)*

This definition includes both the natural (hydrological) and the human (socio-economic) elements of the system and acknowledges the importance and complexity of the linkages between them. The boundary they use is the geographical boundary of the river (drainage) basin. In practice, of course, drainage basin boundaries do not correspond to the political borders between countries, hence the competing demands for the resource and the potential for conflict between countries.

One other example of the use of the word system is in 'ecosystem', which was defined in Block 1 as 'the relationships and interdependence between organisms and their physical environment, and how these relationships function'. A related concept is the idea of ***ecosystem services*** provided by living systems on which we depend. For aquatic ecosystems, which could be anything from an entire river basin to a small pond, these services include production of oxygen by water plants as they photosynthesise; removal of organic wastes by bacteria; and control of flooding by wetlands that 'hold' the water and buffer extreme flows. In addition to these practical services are the aesthetic pleasures derived from rivers, ponds and lakes for recreation and amenity. Aquatic ecosystems require a certain level of both quality and quantity of water to support these services. Fortunately, many ecosystems have a certain amount of resilience to the impacts of human use. But if water is continually or excessively polluted, or if too much is extracted for use by humans, the aquatic ecosystem can be damaged beyond recovery. If humans place too many demands on such an ecosystem, then our use of water becomes unsustainable.

Systems thinking is helpful for many complex situations but is particularly useful for problem solving, when the first step is (or should be) exploring the situation in order to identify exactly what the problem is. Taking a ***systems approach*** to a problematic situation involves taking account of the fact that different stakeholders in a particular situation will recognise different systems within that situation. It also means taking account of the wider context rather than just focusing on one part. It means thinking systemically (considering the whole) rather than only systematically (in a linear, step-by-step way). Failing to consider both these aspects can be a major stumbling block in looking for solutions to environmental problems.

Summary of Section 3

Water is a renewable resource that is in global circulation by the action of the water cycle. People extract water from rivers, lakes and groundwater and, after use, it is usually returned but it is likely to be polluted, unless first treated in a sewage works. Water-borne disease is a major problem in areas with inadequate sanitation. When using water as a resource it is important to consider both quality and quantity. Aquatic ecosystems can be resilient to human impact up to a point but can be damaged if use is unsustainable. Thinking of complex, interrelated situations in terms of systems, in order to define what is or is not included, can be useful.

Ways of getting water

I get the water I need out of a tap – and I expect most of you do too. But how does it get there? It was noted earlier that we get our water by tapping into the water cycle at some point between precipitation on to land and discharge into the sea. We do this by ***abstraction*** from surface waters, such as rivers and lakes, or from groundwater. In the UK, most of the abstracted water is treated to ***potable*** (drinkable) standards in water treatment works. This usually involves several stages of treatment including sedimentation, filtration and chlorination (or some other method of disinfection) to kill any remaining pathogens. On the whole, although occasionally there are accidents and problems with supply, most UK residents can be confident that water supply will always be there 'on tap'. They can also be confident in the quality of the water and know that it is safe to drink. In addition, they have the very obvious advantage that water is piped into their house and does not need to be collected or carried from somewhere else. As you have already seen, for some people in the countries of the Nile basin, this is often not the case.

The next activity focuses on water supply in Ethiopia. You have already seen how water is used in two Ethiopian homes. This section looks more closely at the different ways in which they get their water and how this affects their lives. One of the points to consider when you watch the videos in Activity 1.4 is the use of ***technology*** in water supply. Technology is a familiar word frequently used in the context of computers or other machines and tools but it is important to realise that it means more than just the hardware. It also incorporates the people who are using the tools and how they use them. Most dictionary definitions make this clear. For example, Merriam-Webster's dictionary defines technology not in terms of machines at all but as the 'practical application of knowledge' (Merriam-Webster Online, 2009). From this definition it follows that more advanced technology, if judged only in terms of sophistication or complexity of equipment, is not necessarily better. The people using the technology, or applying the knowledge, need to be considered too. In some cases, very simple technologies, where they are efficient and effective, are still the most appropriate. This idea of appropriate technology is an important one, especially in developing countries, which may not have access to the support and service infrastructure that can usually be assumed in the developed world. Appropriate technologies are those that meet human needs in a sustainable way. They will ideally be instigated by the people who are to benefit from them but if not, the people must at least understand the reasons for installing the technology, how it works, and the implications of using it.

Toilets provide a useful example of appropriate and inappropriate technology. In dry areas, flush toilets can be highly inappropriate. They use a lot of water on each flush that could be better used for more essential purposes. They are relatively expensive to install and run and so likely to result in the relatively well-off using more of the precious water resource at the expense of others. Furthermore, the consequence of using them is frequently to wash human effluent into a watercourse, thereby polluting the water for other uses. In these circumstances, a far more appropriate technology would be pit latrines (Figure 1.2), which consist merely of a pit to contain the waste and use no water (McCully, 1996).

(A related point to note in passing is that in the UK and many other places, the water that is used to flush the toilets is potable water, fully treated to comply with drinking water standards. You may wonder if this is appropriate.)

There is another DVD activity not long after this one, in Section 5.1. If you would rather not go to and fro from your computer, you can do both activities now.

Activity 1.4 Ways of getting water

On the course DVD, go to Block 3, Part 1 and click on 'Ways of getting water'.

Summary of Section 4

Both the quantity and quality of water supplies are influenced by the land use in the surrounding area. Loss of vegetation cover, soil erosion and pollution can all have a negative impact.

For some people, simply getting adequate quantities of water for their daily needs is a major task that takes up a large part of their time. In Ethiopia, many people depend on unprotected sources for their water supply, which leaves them vulnerable to waterbome disease. Others have the benefit of easy access to a clean, safe water supply. Provision of this supply may depend on the development and maintenance of water treatment facilities. Sometimes, less complex water supply systems may be more appropriate and more sustainable.

Ways of using water 5

We all need water to survive. The absolute minimum required by each person varies considerably depending on activity level, climate and diet, but the World Health Organization recommendations for daily requirements of drinking water under average conditions are 2.2 litres for adult females and 2.9 litres for males (Water UK, 2008). You may think that is rather a lot, perhaps more than you usually drink, but it includes water consumed in the food we eat and in other drinks. This is the amount we need on a daily basis to survive as living beings, but there are other ways of looking at the water we use. A much greater amount of water, known as embedded water, is used in the various processes of food production than ends up actually incorporated within the foodstuff itself. We do not directly consume the embedded water into our bodies but we do use it indirectly in food and other products (Box 1.3).

Box 1.3 Embedded water

Embedded water is the water used in the production of food or other products. Also known as virtual water, embodied water, hidden water or shadow water, it means the total amount of water used in the various steps of a production process.

The term is usually used with reference to agricultural products but can also be applied to non-agricultural goods. The quantities of embedded water are derived from the total amount of water required to produce a good from start to finish.

For example, about 3500 litres of water are needed to produce 1 kilogram of rice and about 1000 litres for 1 kilogram of wheat. Beef can require 15 000 litres per kilogram. This amount includes all the water used in the production of beef, such as the water that the animals drink, the amount used to produce grains and grass for feeding them, and an amount for washing down facilities and similar uses in servicing them.

The amounts can vary significantly depending on the country of production and the methods used in production. For example, a kilogram of tomatoes would have an embedded water content of roughly 8 litres if produced in the UK and about 340 litres if produced in Indonesia.

Embedded water becomes particularly significant in the context of global trading of products. Any product exported or imported carries with it an amount of embedded water. The exporting country is effectively exporting water that might otherwise be used to meet its own needs. For countries where water is scarce, this can be a significant loss. Cotton, for example, exported from Egypt to the UK and elsewhere, contains about 9000 litres of embedded water per kilogram.

(Adapted from Waterwise, 2007)

As well as direct consumption, our personal needs include water for washing ourselves and our clothes and dishes, water for food preparation and for sanitation. Estimates of how much water we need to meet these basic needs vary considerably, but lie in the range approximately from 20 litres per person per day (UNDP, 2006) to 50 litres per person per day (Stern, 2007, p. 79; Gleick, 2000, p. 11). It is important to recognise that these are global figures and reflect an estimate of requirements, not necessarily what we actually use. In Activity 1.2 you estimated the amount of water you use for personal and domestic purposes. However, there are, of course, many uses outside the home. The remainder of this section and Section 6 will examine some of the ways in which water is used in the Nile basin.

Table 1.1 shows the quantities of water used by the Nile basin countries, with the UK and USA included for comparison. The volume of water withdrawal is divided into proportions used for domestic, industrial and agricultural purposes.

Study note: data interpretation

Large quantities of data are often best presented in tables. It is often tempting to accept such figures uncritically but there are several possible limitations that you may need to consider when interpreting such data. For example, note that the data in Table 1.1 was published in the year 2000 and is based on figures from several years before that. Always consider the date of publication and the possibility that the figures may be a little dated. Also consider the type of data and how it might have been obtained. The data in Table 1.1, relates to whole countries so would probably have been quite difficult to gather accurately. It is very likely that the figures were actually estimates rather than precise measurements. However, this is not to say that such data is worthless! In this case, the table is presenting comparisons and it is reasonable to assume that similar constraints may have applied across the board. The important point is to recognise the possible limitations and to avoid using such data in a way that suggests a higher degree of accuracy than can safely be assumed, or without quoting its source so this can be checked by others.

Table 1.1 Fresh water withdrawal and use for countries of the Nile basin.

Country	Year on which data is based	Total fresh water withdrawal (km^3 per year)	Estimated population in 2000 (million)	Estimated per capita withdrawal in 2000 (m^3 per person per year)	Use		
					Domestic (%)	Industrial (%)	Agricultural (%)
Burundi	1987	0.10	6.97	14	36	0	64
Democratic Republic of Congo	1990	0.36	51.75	7	61	16	23
Egypt	1993	55.10	68.12	809	6	8	86
Ethiopia (and Eritrea)	1987	2.20	69.99	31	11	3	86
Kenya	1990	2.05	30.34	68	20	4	76
Rwanda	1993	0.77	7.67	100	5	2	94
Sudan	1995	17.80	29.82	597	4	1	94
Tanzania	1994	1.17	33.69	35	9	2	89
Uganda	1970	0.20	22.46	9	32	8	60
UK	1994	11.75	58.34	201	20	77	3
USA	1995	469.00	277.83	1688	12	46	42

Source: Gleick, 2000, Table 2, pp. 205–211.

Water withdrawal means water removed from a source and used for human needs. Not all water withdrawn is necessarily consumed. It may be returned to the original source, possibly with changes in quantity or quality, e.g. water used for cooling in power stations.

SAQ 1.6 Water use in the Nile basin

Which two Nile basin countries use the most water?

Which two use the most per capita (i.e. per head) of population?

Suggest some possible reasons why this might be the case. (It may help to think back to Activity 1.1 on the course DVD.)

SAQ 1.7 Water use data

Based on the data in Table 1.1, what was the estimated water withdrawal in the UK for the year 2000 in litres of water per person per day?

Why might this differ from the figure of 50 litres per person per day of water required, quoted above?

For the Nile basin countries in Table 1.1, the data for the three use categories as percentages of total water withdrawn shows the dominance of agricultural over domestic and industrial use very clearly. In all cases, agriculture is by far the greatest user. The contrast with the relative proportions for UK and USA reinforces this picture. In the UK especially, agricultural use is minimal at only 3% of the total. There are many reasons for this, including the climate, the particular mix of crops and livestock farming in the UK, and the relative importance of industrial use. As the footnote to the table says, industrial use includes water used for cooling in power stations, which is a major 'user' of water in the UK.

Of the three main categories, domestic use has already been discussed, and agricultural use of water for irrigation is the topic for the next section. Withdrawal for industrial purposes, although relatively small for the Nile countries, is nonetheless an important use that can have a major impact on water quality, especially at a local level.

Water is used for many industrial processes in the Nile basin, including sugar cane and cotton processing, especially in Egypt and Sudan. Floriculture, i.e. growing flowers on an industrial scale for export, has grown rapidly over the past 10–15 years. It is now a major source of external income for Kenya, Uganda and Ethiopia, but the industry requires considerable quantities of pesticides and the possible damage to the environment and to workers' health is a cause of concern. The countries that border Lake Victoria use the lake water for many industrial purposes including textile and tannery mills, coffee, cotton and fish processing plants, and cosmetics and soap production. Although much of the water is returned to the river or lake after use, it is frequently heavily polluted. This not only causes ecological damage to the aquatic ecosystem, but also affects the livelihoods of people who depend on the river or lake and affects the usability of the water for those living downstream. As seen in Figure 1.4, this is a potential source of conflict between upstream and downstream users in any river system. In the Nile basin, the sheer size of the river, the volumes of water involved and the dilution this provides make the input of industrial pollution *relatively* unimportant. When considering the basin as a whole, and the availability of water resources, issues of quantity tend to dominate over issues of quality.

5.1 Irrigation

Agricultural irrigation is the artificial distribution of water on to soil for growing crops. In many parts of the world, irrigation turns unusable land into productive agricultural fields. Egypt is essentially a desert country and it would be impossible to grow crops without irrigation water. Irrigation has been fundamental to development in Egypt for millennia. Historically, torrential rain in the Ethiopian highlands would result in the Nile flooding in Egypt roughly between June and September. The waters would spread over the flood plain and when they receded in September or October a rich deposit of silt would remain, making the land very fertile. The irrigation system used in Egypt for centuries was a traditional basin system in which mud embankments were built to create small basins that retained the annual flood water, and the silt that came with it, after the main flood had receded. Although the water was retained for a while, basin irrigation was only possible during, and shortly after, the time of the flood. At other times water had to be raised up from the river channel, which was lower than the irrigation canals. The Egyptians invented some of the earliest devices for lifting water, such as the shaduf and the sakia (Figure 1.16). These simple, and appropriate, technologies are still in use today.

(b)

(a)

Figure 1.16 Two traditional water-lifting devices: (a) the shaduf – a simple lever arrangement in which a wooden beam with a weight at one end and a bucket at the other is lowered and raised in the river; (b) the sakia or saqiya – the ox walks in a circle turning a horizontal cogged wheel; this engages with a vertical cogged wheel with pots attached that dips into the river and discharges water into a channel

The first larger-scale structures built across the river channel to provide irrigation water were the barrages across the two main distributaries of the Nile delta and were constructed in the middle of the nineteenth century. They were designed to hold back the water, especially in summer when flows were low, in order to maintain flow into the irrigation canals. The delta barrages were followed by others, including the two big dams at Aswan: the first, built in 1902, which became known as the Low Aswan Dam and the second, much larger, High Aswan Dam completed in 1970 (see Section 6.1).

The area of cultivated, and hence populated, land in most of Egypt and northern Sudan is defined by the extent of irrigation and so is confined to a ribbon of development along the Nile river (Figure 1.17).

Figure 1.17 Satellite photo of the northern Nile as it flows through Egypt showing the green 'ribbon' along the river and the delta. (If you have Block 1 to hand you might like to compare this with the Block 1 cover picture.)

Irrigation enables cereals including wheat, maize and sorghum to be grown, as well as cotton, vegetables and fruit, and provides the basis of the livelihoods of millions of people. Without irrigation the people would simply not be able to live where they do. In the upper Nile countries, irrigation does not have the crucial role that it does in Egypt and Sudan but nonetheless is still of vital importance to many rural communities.

Activity 1.5 includes a short video that tells the story of a river in Ethiopia used by several neighbouring communities for irrigation. It picks up on the theme of stakeholders that was introduced at the start of this block. The story is about competition for the shared river between upstream and downstream water users and how this has led to conflict between them.

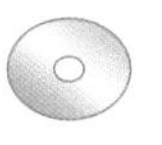

Activity 1.5 Ethiopian river story

On the course DVD, go to Block 3, Part 1 and click on 'Ethiopian river story'.

In some parts of the world, irrigation of agricultural land not only increases the yields of crops and allows cultivation of land that would otherwise be too dry, it also raises land values. (Note that in Ethiopia, land is owned by the state, not by individuals.) This can be especially important to large landowners who have the resources to invest in machinery, chemicals and labour that enable maximum use of the water resources. These wealthy landowners also have more marketing power and influence and are able to ensure that they get their full share of the limited water and maximise their profits from the land. Small farmers, on the other hand, are often working at subsistence level, that is, they can only grow enough to meet the needs of themselves and their families. With less capital and less power, they are not in a position to profit from increased land values and are also highly vulnerable to unpredictable events such as drought and flood.

5.1.1 Salinisation and waterlogging

Salinisation and waterlogging are undesirable consequences of poorly managed irrigation systems in hot climates. In Egypt, nearly a third of all farmland has been affected in this way and crop yields in these areas have fallen by about 30% as a result (El-Ashry, 1993).

All irrigation waters contain a certain amount of dissolved salts derived from the rocks through which the water passes. The salts will be a variety of chemical compounds, depending on the local geology, and are likely to include sodium and calcium salts (see Box 1.4). If water is standing in reservoirs, canals and fields this exposes a large surface area to the heat of the Sun. Water evaporates from the surface so the remaining solution becomes more and more concentrated (saline). Plants take up water as they grow but leave most of the salt molecules behind, thereby increasing concentration even more. The salinity of the soil solution can get so high that it disrupts water uptake and becomes toxic to most plants, leading to diminished crop yields.

Box 1.4 Salts, solutions and concentration

Salts

The white crystalline substance used in cooking that we call salt is, in chemical terms, sodium chloride. That is, it is a chemical compound made of the elements sodium and chlorine. This is just one of many salts which, in chemistry, is a term applied to many compounds. Some salts are soluble in water, others are not.

The 'saltiness' of sea water is caused by a mixture of salts. Sodium chloride is the major constituent but it also includes small amounts of magnesium chloride, sodium sulphate, calcium chloride and potassium chloride.

Solution

When a substance dissolves in water it forms a ***solution***. The molecules of the dissolved substance are completely mixed with the water molecules (H_2O) but it is possible to reverse this process and reconstitute the substance from the solution. For example, if you dissolved a teaspoon of sugar in a cup of water, the solid sugar would disappear as it dissolves in the water. If you then heated the sugar solution for long enough, the water would evaporate leaving the solid sugar behind.

Concentration

Concentration is a measure of the amount of substance dissolved in a known volume of a solution. Various units are used, including g m^{-3} (grams per cubic metre), mg/l or mg l^{-1} (milligrams per litre); per cent (parts per 100 units of solution); ppm (parts per million) and ppb (parts per billion).

To remedy the situation, farmers often try to flush the salts away with more water. This washes the salts down into the groundwater but if the ***water table*** rises with increasing application of water, the salty water rises to the surface. More evaporation exacerbates the problem and can lead to a salty crust developing on the surface. The excess water remains in the top layers of soil, where the plant roots are, and this waterlogging inhibits plant growth. To prevent this, good drainage is an essential part of any irrigation system. This is the same principle as having drainage holes in the bottom of flowerpots. The plants need water, but if oxygen from the air cannot reach the roots because they are waterlogged, the plant will suffer and eventually die. Any effective irrigation system therefore not only needs to supply water but also needs adequate drainage so that the excess water has somewhere to go. Without it, trying to solve the salinity problem by using more water to wash away the excess salts will only make things worse. An alternative approach could be to use less water and try to ensure that only just enough for crop growth is supplied. One way to achieve this is to use drip or trickle irrigation methods rather than traditional uncontrolled supply. These minimise water use by allowing only a small amount to be released at a time.

5.2 Fisheries

The domestic, industrial and agricultural uses discussed so far all require removal of water from its source, but we use water in many other ways that do not take water from the natural system.

Many thousands of people living on the Nile rivers and lakes depend on fish for their livelihoods or as part of their food supply. For example, fisheries have long been a very important part of the local economy around

Lake Victoria. Named by Speke after Queen Victoria, this is the second largest freshwater lake in the world in terms of surface area (after Lake Superior in the USA) and is shared by Uganda, Tanzania and Kenya. The lake is fished commercially from canoes, mostly for Nile perch and Nile tilapia (Figure 1.18).

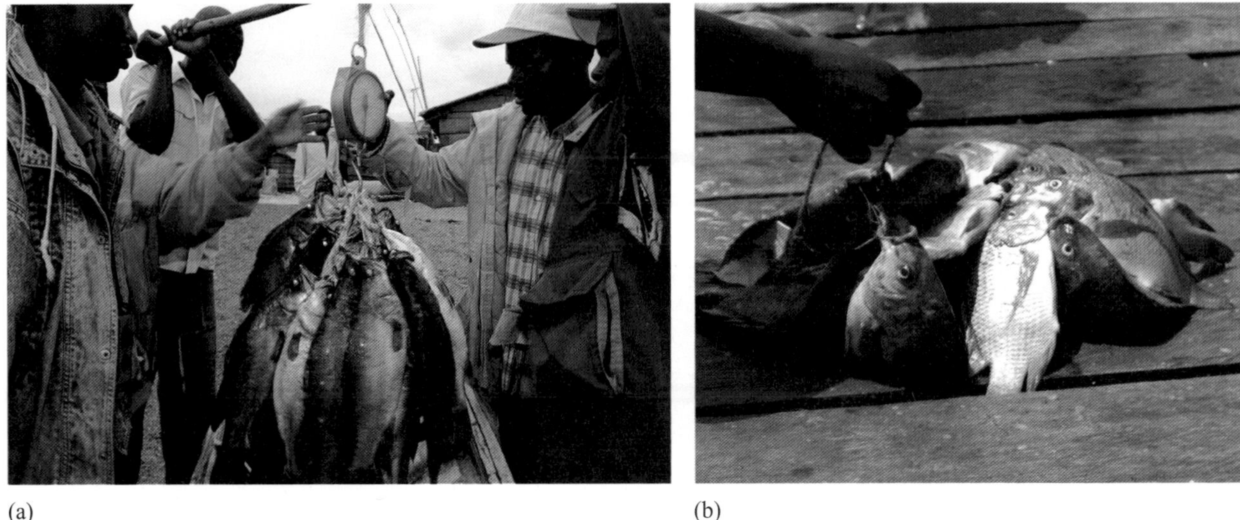

(a) (b)

Figure 1.18 Fishing on Lake Victoria: (a) Nile perch; (b) Nile tilapia

These species were introduced in the 1950s and 1960s and for many years supported an expanding and profitable fishing industry on the shores of the lake. The perch and tilapia populations thrived but at the cost of the over 500 native fish species, many of which were eaten by the predatory Nile perch. The fishing industry expanded and attracted more fishers and more investment, and led to the construction of processing plants around the lake. By the end of the 1990s the yield of Nile perch alone was more than 1 million tonnes per year. Seventy-five per cent of this was exported to Europe, the USA and the Middle East, providing a significant source of income for the three riparian countries. However, since then the catch has reduced to little more than half that amount (Mukyala, 2008). Uncontrolled and unsustainable expansion of fishing has depleted the commercial fish stocks. The decline in fishing has been a significant cause of poverty and many fishermen are having to try to find other means to support themselves and their families. On the other hand, from an ecological perspective, the decline in the perch has seen some recovery in the populations of the native fish.

5.3 Transport, tourism and wildlife

The Nile river and its lakes have for centuries provided a communication route and means of transport for people living on and near the watercourse. Originally mostly for transporting local people and goods, river boats of one sort or another are increasingly used to transport tourists. Luxury cruise boats ply up and down the lower Nile in Egypt between Luxor and the High Aswan Dam (Figure 1.19(a)). Lake Nasser, created by the dam, is a popular location for sport fishing and also attracts tourists interested in the temples of Ancient Egypt. White-water kayaking and rafting are increasingly popular activities in Uganda, where several companies offer trips near the Bujagali Falls (Figure 1.19(b) and (c)). Even bungee jumping over the river is available.

(a)

(b)

(c)

Figure 1.19 Leisure activities on the River Nile: (a) cruising; (b) white-water kayaking; (c) rafting

The sights and sounds of the river itself are spectacular and, combined with the wildlife, make for a memorable holiday destination. For example, in the Murchison Falls National Park, in northern Uganda, you can not only visit the magnificent falls but also see crocodile, hippo, elephant, lion, giraffe and much more, and relax in a luxury hotel on the banks of the river (Figure 1.20).

Clearly, transport and tourism do not 'use' the river water in the same way as agriculture and industry but they still have an environmental impact. For example, waste discarded from boats can pollute the water. Hotels with

Figure 1.20 Murchison Falls National Park, Uganda

many bathrooms, lush gardens and swimming pools can place great demands on water resources in order to meet the assumed expectations of tourists. If water resources are limited, then meeting these expectations can mean there is less water available for the local residents and the local wildlife. But tourism also has many benefits. It brings in much-needed external income and can provide significant material benefits at both national and local community levels (as you will see in Part 2 of this block). However, it is not only monetary value that needs to be considered. The river, waterfalls and lakes all have an environmental value derived from the habitats they provide and the wildlife they support. Part 2 explores these different meanings of value and the pros and cons of tourism and its environmental impact in more detail.

Underlying all of this is the fact that the animals, plants and entire aquatic ecosystems are another 'user' of water that should not be overlooked. Without adequate supplies of clean water the continued existence of aquatic habitats would be compromised. Any management of water resources to ensure fair allocation to meet the needs of all users should also consider the needs of the environment.

Summary of Section 5

Water is used for many different purposes, not only to meet domestic needs but also for agriculture and industry. In many parts of the Nile basin, irrigation is essential for crop growth and it is the largest use of water in the region. However, in some locations, poor irrigation management practices have led to salinisation and waterlogging of the soil. Other, non-extractive, uses of water such as fisheries, transport and tourism provide valuable income but these too have environmental impacts. Aquatic ecosystems depend on adequate quantities of good quality water for their continued existence and this can be compromised by some human activities.

6 Dams

Dams are built to enable water to be used by people, so could have been included in the previous section about ways of using water, but they are such an important environmental issue that they merit a section in their own right. Large dams have been, and continue to be, highly contentious and are among the most bitterly contested development projects throughout the world. Estimates vary, but there are several hundred currently under construction, principally in developing countries. There are many benefits from building dams but there are disadvantages too, and this is where controversy and conflict can arise.

6.1 Costs and benefits of dams

Dams have two principal functions that enable many of the uses described in Section 5. One is to store water in a reservoir behind the dam and the other is to raise the water level and thus create a 'hydraulic head'. The head is the difference in height between the reservoir and the river immediately downstream. The creation of storage and head can be used to meet the following needs:

- to generate electricity in a hydroelectric power (HEP) scheme (see Box 1.5)
- to direct water from rivers into canals for irrigation and water supply
- to control flooding downstream of the dam by regulating the river flow to reduce seasonal fluctuations
- to assist river navigation below the dam, again by regulating the river flow
- to provide reservoir fisheries, boating and leisure opportunities.

All of these can bring benefits and profoundly affect economic prosperity. Improved power, agriculture, water supply and recreation opportunities will all contribute to the productivity of the region. The incentives for dam building are easy to see but there are costs – financial, social and environmental.

Box 1.5 Hydroelectric power

In a hydroelectric power (HEP) plant, electricity is generated by permitting a controlled flow of high-velocity water through a channel called the penstock. The velocity depends on there being a sufficient drop, the 'hydraulic head', between the top and bottom of the water flow. The water spins the turbines that turn the generators, producing an electric current (Figure 1.21). This current then goes via transmission lines to a substation, where the voltage is reduced before distribution to domestic and other users.

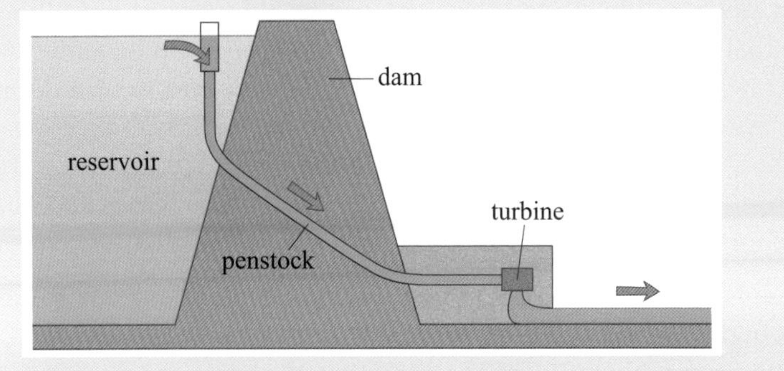

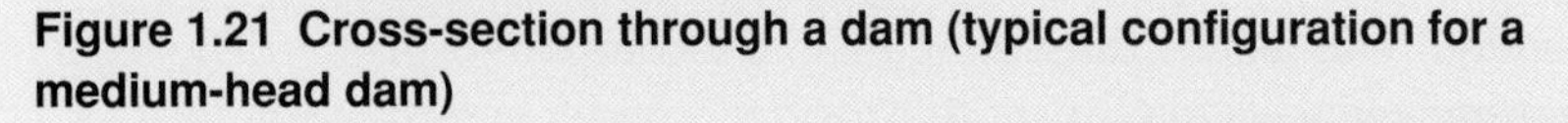

Figure 1.21 Cross-section through a dam (typical configuration for a medium-head dam)

In many cases, HEP plants are associated with dams and reservoirs built to create the necessary hydraulic head, although on some rivers the normal flow is adequate. In either case water is diverted into the plant and then returned further downstream. The benefit of HEP is that it is a form of renewable energy, but the construction of dams and reservoirs and the draw-off of water from its natural course can have significant environmental impacts.

The productive capacity of HEP (and other) generating plants is usually measured in terms of megawatts (MW), e.g. a 250 MW power station. A megawatt is one million (10^6) watts (W). The watt is the SI unit for power, which is the rate at which energy is delivered. Energy is measured in joules, and a watt is a rate of energy output of 1 joule per second. A 250 MW power station, therefore, is capable of producing 250×10^6 joules of energy per second.

Dams and other major development projects are often assessed in terms of cost–benefit analysis. Cost–benefit analysis is a form of economic model that purports to calculate the costs and benefits associated with a particular project or decision in purely monetary terms. You may be familiar with the sorts of numbers that appear in the economic case presented to support major developments such as new roads, airports or dams. What you may not have wondered is exactly how these numbers are derived, since they can seem so absolute and authoritative. Yet these numbers are actually based on a whole host of assumptions that may or may not be reasonable. A particular issue that arises with major projects such as dams is the question of timing. Building a dam involves large costs that are incurred immediately, but the benefits accrue over the lifetime of the dam, maybe tens or hundreds of years. This raises questions about how the costs incurred today are compared with the benefits (and possibly more costs) that come next year, the year after, and so on for a long period. Is a benefit of £100 million, which is obtained between now and ten years hence, really worth £10 million more than the perhaps £90 million cost of the dam laid out today? In fact, economists have accountancy techniques (specifically ***discounting***) that in effect reduce the value of future costs and benefits according to how long into the future they occur. So a benefit of £1 million in year 10 of a project is supposed to be worth less than a £1 million cost incurred at the start. This seems fair, but the factor used to reduce the value of future cash sums can be controversial. The technique also biases decisions in favour of shorter-term benefits, and downplays long-term costs.

A second issue with such economic evaluations is the boundary put around the system being considered in the costings. If the system is deemed to involve only the company building the dam, then the costs and benefits considered will just be those that affect the company's profits. The local governing agencies may want to consider a wider system boundary, including costs and benefits to all (or more probably some) of their constituents. Environmental campaigners are likely to look to an even wider system boundary, and want the costs and benefits to local wildlife or even to the whole biosphere to be taken into account. Depending on the system chosen, the economics can look very different. Analyses of this sort underpin most major decisions, and you should always look carefully at the assumptions underlying such analyses before accepting the economic data as being unassailable.

In the Nile region, the earliest dams were constructed around 2500 BC and many others followed. The first large dam was completed at Aswan in 1902 when Egypt was under British control. The British sought to convert the local self-supporting peasant farming practices into large-scale irrigated agriculture producing high-value crops such as cotton. The enormous annual fluctuations in the flow of the Nile and the variation in flow between years led to the decision that controlling the flow by building a dam was necessary. The British colonial power's attitude to the use of water resources is revealed in this quotation from Winston Churchill, who was a young, newly appointed UK Government minister at the time:

> One day, every last drop of water which drains into the whole valley of the Nile … shall be equally and amicably divided among the river people, and the Nile itself … shall perish gloriously and never reach the sea.
>
> *(Winston Churchill, 1908, quoted in McCully, 1996, p. 18)*

Churchill's wish may have been for amicable sharing but, as noted in Section 2, this was not the case, at least not at that time. (This is speculation, but it is quite possible that his idea of 'river people' was only those in Egypt.) We may find his description of the death of the Nile by using up all the water as 'glorious' rather difficult to accept but this was the prevailing attitude at the time. Water was there to be used and any environmental

concerns were simply not considered. Things have moved on since then, but economic justification often still prevails over environmental and social impacts. A similar conflict between economics and the environment can be seen in the changes to the Blue Nile falls or Tis Isat ('water that smokes'), a few miles from Lake Tana in Ethiopia. In the recent past, the falls created a perpetual mist that supported a localised spray-dependent ecosystem and dense forest grew right up to the edge of the falls. Much of this has now gone. A few years ago a hydro-electric power plant providing much needed electricity was built adjacent to the falls and since then, the draw-off of water to supply the turbines has significantly reduced the river volume. Water is taken off above the falls and returns below so the width of the falls has reduced and there is far less spray than there used to be.
Figure 1.22 shows 'before' and 'after' views of the falls.

(a)

(b)

Figure 1.22 (a) the Ethiopian 1 birr note shows the former full width of the Blue Nile falls and the lush forest growing right up to the edge of the falls; (b) In contrast, the falls today are narrower and the area that was formerly forest (top right) has been brought into cultivation

6.2 Two dams compared

This section consists of two examples of large dams on the Nile – High Aswan in Egypt, built in the 1960s, and the current project at Bujagali in Uganda. Each has one or two SAQs on particular aspects of the story. You may want to look at the Study note: *reading with a purpose* in Block 1 before reading further.

6.2.1 High Aswan Dam

The height of the 1902 Low Aswan Dam was increased twice in the early twentieth century but it still did not have enough capacity in the reservoir to contain the flood waters in some years. A new dam was proposed and, following the Nile Water Agreement of 1959 between Egypt and Sudan, construction of the High Aswan Dam began.

Figure 1.23 High Aswan Dam, looking east: the River Nile, flowing northwards to the Mediterranean, is on the left and Lake Nasser is behind the dam on the right

The High Aswan Dam (Figure 1.23), completed in 1970, is about 6 km north (downstream) of the 1902 dam. Its embankment is 111 m high and extends nearly 1000 m in width. The lake that gradually filled the valley behind it after the dam was closed is 480 km long and up to 16 km wide. The lake is named Lake Nasser, after Gamal Abdel Nasser, who was president of Egypt at the time and died the year the dam was finished. Construction of the dam was largely funded by the Soviet Union, which also provided technical services and support.

The political situation at the time is described by Patrick McCully:

> In July 1952 a group of army officers headed by Colonel Gamal Abdel Nasser overthrew Egypt's King Farouk. Soon after taking power, the Revolutionary Command Council became fixated by a proposal [...] for a huge dam across the Nile at Aswan. The supposed purpose of the dam was to iron out the great river's yearly cycle of floods and droughts, expand irrigation and produce electricity. Perhaps even more important, however, was the political

significance to the young, revolutionary government of undertaking such an audacious endeavour. Historian John Waterbury says that:

> Politically it had the advantage of being gigantic and daring, thrusting Egypt into the vanguard of modern hydraulic engineering. Moreover, during its construction and after its completion, it would be highly visible and fittingly monumental.

The Revolutionary Command Council's determination to build the dam, and their concept of it as a monument to national pride, was passed on to the rest of the government, and to the Egyptian people. Officials who had once questioned the viability of the project changed their minds or kept quiet. An official from the Ministry of Public Works explained the atmosphere at the time by quoting from the *Rubáiyát of Omar Khayyám*: 'When the King says it is midnight at noon, the wise man says behold the moon.'[Waterbury, 1979, pp. 99, 101]

The primacy of the political motivations for building the high dam at Aswan is evidenced by the paucity of investigations into the dam's likely benefits and costs. According to US political scientists Robert Rycroft and Joseph Szyliowicz, the economic justification of the dam was based on calculations 'clearly of doubtful validity' which 'were based on very rough estimates that had been gathered in the first flush of enthusiasm for the project and were never refined'. The economic analysis of High Aswan 'ignored accepted means of assessing projects, particularly in the field of water resources, for which an extensive literature was available'. Agricultural benefits, for example, were calculated without any thorough surveys of the quality of the land to be brought under irrigation, and without taking account of the cost of providing the necessary canals and other irrigation infrastructure. Similarly, added Rycroft and Szyliowicz, 'no study ever evaluated the cost of generating power through the High Dam or compared it to the construction of thermal power stations'. Although many of the [subsequent] costs of the dam were anticipated, none was included in its economic analysis. [Rycroft and Szyliowicz, 1980]

In late 1955, spurred by reports that the Soviet Union was also keen to help Nasser build the dam and so strengthen its influence in Africa, the World Bank and the American and British governments put together a funding package for the project. The Western proposal came with a number of conditions, including one requiring that the Egyptian government avoid 'imprudent' financial decisions – in part a reference to arms purchases from the Soviet bloc. Furious at the conditions, Nasser rejected the offer. Seven months of fruitless negotiations followed, at the end of which the Western powers withdrew their proposal. Soon after, Nasser used what he saw as the West's insulting colonialist behaviour as a justification for seizing the Suez Canal, setting off the brief 1956 war with Israel, Britain and France.

The Suez crisis and the dispute over financing Aswan firmly established Egypt in the Soviet camp, and the dam was finally built with technical assistance and money from the USSR. It also enshrined the dam as a nationalist icon. According to Waterbury, 'Nasser and his associates could no longer regard the dam as simply a big engineering project, but rather came to hold it up as the symbol of Egypt's will to resist imperialist endeavours to destroy the revolution.' The pro-dam fervour was such that crowds gathered outside the Egyptian parliament and chanted: 'Nasser, Nasser, we come to salute you; after the Dam our land will be paradise'. [Waterbury, 1979, p. 116]

(McCully, 1996, pp. 238–9)

Study note: summarising

A summary – or précis – is a shorter version of a longer piece of writing. It should contain the main points of the original text and should be an easy-to-read version of the original, written in your own words. The technique when reading a long piece of text is to take notes, as previously described, which bring out the key pieces of information in the text. This is the first step to obtaining a shorter, but structured, overview of the main ideas and arguments. You can then link together the key points from the notes using sentences or paragraphs as appropriate.

SAQ 1.8 Summarising

Summarise the main points from the McCully extract. Use proper sentences but limit your summary to approximately 100 words.

Work began on the dam in 1960. International interest was not only concerned with the politics of the situation but also the loss of several ancient monuments and archaeological sites that would be submerged by the impending reservoir. A major rescue mission was initiated to relocate the monuments above the water line. Twenty monuments from Egypt and four from Sudan were dismantled and re-erected in locations that would not be flooded (Figure 1.24).

(a) (b)

Figure 1.24 Moving the Abu Simbel temple: (a) a face is reunited with its body, September 1966; (b) reconstructed figures view Lake Nasser from safely above the water line

The area flooded by Lake Nasser is a part of Egypt and Sudan that was formerly Nubia, a country in its own right. In fact, in Sudan the lake is called Lake Nubia, not Lake Nasser. The Egyptian government made arrangements for the Nubians to be relocated, but their lifestyle was destroyed. More than 90 000 people were forced into new settlements and in Sudan, the main Nubian city of Wadi Halfa was submerged. Many of the nomadic tribes in the area were not warned of the changes that would be happening to the river, which affected their routines in caring for their livestock. Prior to the appearance of Lake Nasser, the Nubians cultivated plots along the shore in areas now completely under water. A new city, New Halfa, was created in the eastern desert but many people have since left the new settlements and returned to the lake's edge, trying to recreate their lost culture.

What else has happened since the dam was built? There have been many benefits. The hydropower plant at the dam provides about half of Egypt's electricity. This has decreased the need for other energy sources such as oil. The enormous storage volume has evened out the variations in river flow, so the annual floods have been controlled and no longer present any danger. Irrigation has been facilitated. Seasonal basin irrigation has been replaced with perennial irrigation over 3 million hectares, allowing year-round crop growth. Reclamation of desert has brought new land into cultivation. Control of flooding has also led to improved navigation in the river below the dam, allowing improved transportation of goods and people. Lake Nasser has a flourishing commercial fishery. Nile perch and other fish species thrive in the lake and have provided a more consistent fish yield than was possible before the dam was built (Wiebe, 2001). Another change has been to Egypt's attitude to the water resources of the whole Nile basin. With the construction of the High Aswan Dam, Egypt had a controlled and regular water supply and so the 'obsession with timely or summer water came to an end' (Waterbury, 1979, p. 119). This moderated their need to exercise power and authority over Sudan, making for greater understanding between the two countries, and potentially the other upstream countries.

But there have been disadvantages as well. Evaporation from the surface of Lake Nasser, built in a hot and windy location, is, on average, 11.2 km^3 of water each year, about 10% of the water stored in the reservoir (McCully, 1996). For several years after construction there was also significant loss by seepage into the rocks beneath the reservoir, although this reduced as sediment accumulated at the bottom of the lake. The accumulating sediment is another drawback. Before construction of the dam the annual floodwaters brought an average of 124 million tonnes of silt, clay and sand down the river to the sea each year and deposited another 9.5 million tonnes on the flood plain and in the delta (McCully, 1996, p. 34). Nowadays, more than 98% of the river's sediment load is deposited in Lake Nasser. This has not only significantly reduced the effective volume of the lake but also reduced the fertility of the flood plains below. The sediment provided an annual top-up of essential ***plant nutrients*** (mostly potassium, phosphorus and ***trace elements***) to the cultivated areas of the flood plain that maintained soil fertility. This loss of natural sources has led to increased use of manufactured fertilisers.

The flood waters also maintained the delta, which depended on the constant replenishment of sediment. The effects on the delta have been described by McCully:

> The loss of sediment is particularly significant in the delta, an area the size of Northern Ireland which constitutes two-thirds of Egypt's cropland. Deltas are formed by the accumulation of tens of thousands of years of deposits of river sediments, partly counteracted by their settling and compaction and by erosion from the sea. Remove the incoming sediment, and the land will subside and be eaten away. The slow accretion of the Nile Delta was reversed with the construction of the Delta Barrage in 1868. Other dams built on the Nile throughout the twentieth century further reduced the sediment reaching the delta, but it was only with the building of the High [Aswan] Dam that the Nile all but ceased to wash sediments into the Mediterranean. Today the Nile no longer has a true delta.
>
> *(McCully, 1996, p. 35)*

The loss of sediment carried by the river water also causes scouring or erosion downstream of the dam. The flow of the natural, pre-dam river would cause erosion of the banks and river bed, especially during the annual flood, but this would be balanced by deposition from the river's sediment load. Without the sediment there was nothing to replace the eroded areas, resulting in scouring and lowering of the river bed.

The improved and extended irrigation, though a great benefit, has also had its downside. Perennial irrigation, made possible by the High Aswan Dam, increased the volume of water used and led to greatly increased salinity and waterlogging problems. A contributory factor was that much of the reclaimed desert land was slightly higher than the flood plain and so irrigation water drained back to the lower land, raising the water table and the concentration of dissolved salts. These problems were compounded by the fact that the generous water availability made possible by the dam caused farmers to be more profligate with it and use even more. The solution to salinisation and waterlogging, as noted earlier, was to improve the drainage. This has been successfully achieved in some places but at a financial cost and loss of cultivatable land to drainage ditches.

Human health was also affected. The expanded area of irrigation provided plenty of still water in reservoirs and irrigation canals that created an excellent habitat for water plants and hence the snails that carry schistosomiasis. Added to this, the year-round operation meant that the peasant farmers spent more time in the water. It also saw the end of the annual fallow season when fields were allowed to dry out and the snails would die off. As a consequence of all these factors, the level of schistosomiasis in the population of Egypt increased significantly during the 1970s and 80s (Wiebe, 2001).

McCully goes on to describe other consequences from the dam.

> Nutrients carried to the sea during the flood season once caused a huge bloom of plankton at the mouth of the Nile. This plankton was grazed by great shoals of sardines which accounted for 30–40% of the annual Egyptian sea catch. After the closure of the High Aswan Dam and the elimination of the annual flood, however, the sardine catch fell from 18,000 tonnes to less than a thousand tonnes in the late 1960s. The catch has since risen to a few thousand tonnes but this is attributed to improvements in fishing technology and greater numbers of boats. Shrimp catches at the mouth of the Nile decreased by two-thirds after the nutrient supplies were cut off. Landings of other fish in 1970 were 77% below pre-dam levels.
>
> *(McCully, 1996, p. 45)*

> The increased clarity of the Nile due to the virtual elimination of its silt by the High Aswan Dam has caused a proliferation of algae and phytoplankton in the river. This has fouled the water supply of Cairo and other riverine cities and necessitated an increased use of chlorination.
>
> *(McCully, 1996, p. 150)*

phytoplankton: microscopic floating plants.

SAQ 1.9 High Aswan Dam

List the benefits derived from the High Aswan Dam. What unforeseen, less desirable, consequences did it have?

6.2.2 Bujagali Falls

The Bujagali Falls lie a few kilometres north of Lake Victoria on the White Nile, often called the Victoria Nile in this stretch. The falls are not a waterfall in the conventional sense but are a series of white-water rapids that are increasingly popular with tourists for rafting (Figure 1.25). They also have spiritual significance to the local people.

The Bujagali Dam project, conceived in 1994, has had a controversial history. An earlier scheme failed when corruption was exposed, but the project was finally given the go-ahead and construction commenced in 2007 by a new development company called Bujagali Energy Limited (BEL). The dam's primary purpose is to provide electricity for Uganda, which suffers a severe power shortage. In Kampala, the capital, and other major cities power cuts are frequent because demand outstrips supply. However, only 5% of the population have access to electricity because most rural areas are not connected to the grid, so part of the problem is access to supply rather than supply itself.

Uganda is currently almost entirely dependent for electricity on two HEP plants near Jinja where the Nile leaves Lake Victoria. The Owen Falls Dam (now Nalubaale Power Station) was built in 1954 and this was followed in 2002 by the Kiira power plant nearby. Both these power stations are

Figure 1.25 Bujagali Falls

operating below capacity because the water level in Lake Victoria has fallen significantly since 2003 (for reasons explored below in Section 6.2), which has reduced the generating capability of the plant.

The Bujagali project is highly controversial in Uganda and also among environmental activists around the world. In comparison with other big dam projects, the number of people directly affected is relatively small because there will be not be a huge reservoir created behind the dam that would flood homes and villages. Impact on displaced people may not be the major issue here, but there are many other objections.

The following two articles present two contrasting views of the project. The first is an online report about the laying of the dam's foundation stone from the World Bank, which has provided funds for the project. The second is an article from the UK's *Guardian* newspaper. As you read these two articles consider the perspectives of the authors and how these may influence the tone, content and language.

Uganda's President and the Aga Khan cut ribbon on Bujagali Dam Project

Christopher Walsh and Steven Shalita

The World Bank, 21 August 2007

On August 21 [2007], Uganda's President Yoweri Museveni and the Aga Khan, Prince Karim al-Hussaini, spiritual leader of the Ismaili Muslims, laid the foundation stone for the Bujagali hydropower dam on the Nile River in a show of commitment to address Uganda's continuing energy crisis. The 250 MW project, co-financed by the World Bank Group, is a major component of Uganda's answer to an electricity supply gap that in recent years has made rolling blackouts a daily reality for Ugandan residents, businesses, and services.

rolling blackout: intentional power cut that affects specific areas in rotation, usually for a few hours at a time, in order to share out supply.

The Aga Khan's Fund for Economic Development supports the Bujagali project through its subsidiary development firm, Industrial Promotion Services (Kenya), which, along with Sithe Global (U.S.), comprises the project's development company, Bujagali Energy Limited or BEL.

With the Aga Khan at his side, Museveni urged other African leaders and development partners to face the reality that the continent suffers an energy crisis, which is not only the largest impediment to economic growth, but also at the root of major environmental and other development challenges.

Addressing environmental critics, the president reiterated that the environmental aspects of the Bujagali Project had been extensively studied and debated.

'I wish to assure the public that the Government of Uganda, working with the project sponsor, BEL will ensure that all the identified mitigation measures are satisfactorily implemented,' Museveni said.

He maintained that, while it is important to address legitimate concerns raised about the impact of the dam on the local environment, the project is necessary for Uganda's development.

'You cannot claim to be protecting the environment when you are denying over 90 percent of the population access to electricity,' he said.

Museveni said hydro power is a cheaper alternative than thermal energy, which is presently being used to address the power shortage.

Bujagali is the largest single private sector investment in East Africa, the biggest independent power project in sub-Saharan Africa, as well as the largest single project ever funded by the International Finance Corporation (IFC) in the world, the Aga Khan said in his speech to media and others attending the event. ...

The project is expected to provide badly-needed electricity, boost industry and provide employment for local people during the construction phase as well as later on in the industry and service sectors, according to Uganda's Minister of Energy and Mineral Development Hon. Daudi Migereko.

The Bujagali site is located roughly eight kilometers downstream from the source of the Nile in Lake Victoria and the existing Nalubaale and Kiira hydropower plants. As a run-of-river hydropower facility, the dam will re-use the water flowing from the upstream power plants to generate additional electricity.

run-of-river hydropower facility: where natural river flow is used to generate electricity. It is feasible for rivers with consistent year round flow and does not require a large reservoir to regulate flow

The added power is expected to increase the supply to the national power grid at the lowest cost compared to other power generation options under Uganda's energy sector expansion strategy. ...

The Bujagali Hydropower Project has undergone extensive economic, environmental, and social due diligence. Documents made available to the public include the Project Economic Analysis – prepared by an independent consultant – and the Power Purchase Agreement. Consultations between BEL and communities surrounding the dam site have been ongoing throughout the project.

White water torrent to die as nation gambles on huge Nile dam project

Climate change fears dampen hopes of power from tourist attraction

Xan Rice

The Guardian, 31 May 2007

Six miles north of Lake Victoria, the Nile awakens, exploding into a cauldron of white water known as the Bujagali Falls. Offering some of the world's most spectacular rafting, it is one of Uganda's top attractions. Soon it will be destroyed.

After 13 years of seeing plans delayed by corruption allegations, financial strife, obdurate spirits and opposition from environmental groups, Uganda last week authorised an international consortium to begin a 30-metre-high dam across the Nile just below Bujagali Falls.

The $800m (£400m) hydropower project – the biggest-ever foreign investment in east Africa – will flood the rapids and, according to critics, leave the country dangerously exposed to an energy crisis if predictions of global warming are realised. But the government and the World Bank, which is backing the project with $360m in loans and guarantees, insist that it is crucial to the country's development. 'When the dam is finished [in 2011] we will be rid of the darkness,' said Daudi Migereko, Uganda's energy minister, at the ceremony to approve construction.

In Uganda, where only one in 20 households has access to electricity, nobody doubts that desperate measures are required to solve the chronic power shortage. Even in the energy ministry, lights are often off. Factories have had to cut back production and lay off workers, slowing economic growth. In the capital, Kampala, which hums with the sound of generators, streetlights have been fitted with wind-turbines and solar panels to ensure they are not redundant.

At first glance, harnessing the power of a natural, clean and seemingly abundant energy resource such as the Nile seems logical – and not only to Uganda. In Ethiopia, source of the Blue Nile, Chinese engineers are building the 300MW Tekeze Dam on a Nile tributary and the government has plans for dozens more large dams. In Sudan, where the Blue Nile and White Nile meet at the capital, Khartoum, construction is advanced at the giant 1,250 MW Merowe Dam.

But huge hydropower schemes come with similar risks. As the World Commission on Dams – a joint project of the World Bank and the World Conservation Union – reported in 2000, the social, environmental and financial cost of big dams often outweigh benefits. Merowe, which has displaced 50,000 people and submerged a rich archeological site, is a case in point. Bujagali, according to environmentalists such as Lori Pottinger, Africa director at the US-based International Rivers Network, is another. 'Uganda is making itself wholly dependent on a stretch of river for its electricity,' she said. 'No northern country would accept such a situation.'

Disturbing spirits

Though Bujagali Dam will only displace a few hundred families, the project proved contentious from its inception in 1994. Traditional leaders said it would disturb spirits. Tour operators protested that their livelihoods would be lost.

Critics said that the original contractor, US power company AES, which was to own and operate the dam, stood to make huge profits. A bribery scandal involving a contractor and a senior Uganda World Bank official further muddied its image, and few people were surprised when AES abandoned the project in 2003, citing financial difficulties.

Still, the Ugandan government was not about to give up. In 2005, IPS Kenya, part of the Aga Khan's group of companies, and Sithe Global Power, owned by the giant US private equity firm Blackstone, formed a joint venture called Bujagali Energy to take over the scheme.

But the controversy was just heating up. A devastating drought had hit east Africa, and the level of Lake Victoria, the main source of the Nile, had dropped sharply. The Ugandan government blamed evaporation and decreased river inflows. But independent experts reported that more than half of the drop was man-made. Nearly all Uganda's electricity capacity comes from Nalubaale and Kiira Dams, a short paddle upstream from Bujagali, where the Nile drains out of Lake Victoria. In an attempt to produce more power to cope with increased demand, engineers had made excessive releases through the dam wall, causing more than half of the drop in the lake.

Though Lake Victoria has risen slightly since last year, its low level means that the dams are producing less than a third of their capacity – the main reason for the power crisis. Frank Muramuzi, head of Uganda's National Association of Professional Environmentalists (Nape), said there were severe doubts that future river flows would allow Bujagali Dam to produce near its 250MW capacity. 'We say output will be closer to 100MW, which will make the power far too expensive' he said.

Smaller, cheaper options such as micro-hydro, solar and geothermal projects located in areas that would be of more benefit to the rural poor have not been adequately explored, he said.

But Bujagali Energy denied this. Kenneth Kaheru, technical coordinator for the company, said that though the cost of building the dam had risen to $800m – which would have to be recouped from consumers through higher tariffs – it was still the least costly, and best, option. 'This is a clean project, with minimal impacts. The detractors just don't want dams to be built anywhere.'

Dark days ahead

Fred Kabagambe-Kalissa, an energy official, agreed, comparing environmental groups to 'religious groups who see stopping dams a cause worth dying for'. The economy was losing $250m a year because of the power shortage, he said.

And World Bank officials in Kampala downplayed the possible effects of climate change on Nile's flow, arguing that the fall in the level of Lake Victoria was cyclical. They also dismissed arguments that Uganda's poor will see no benefit from the dams. If the Uganda economy benefits from a more reliable energy supply, they said, everybody will win.

But Godfrey Buyera, who takes tourists around Bujagali rapids on his motorboat, does not feel like a winner. Like others – guides, acrobats, and swimmers who for £2 hurl themselves into rapids clutching a jerry-can – he sees dark days ahead. 'We are going to lose our jobs and we never have electricity in our houses. How are we going to earn when the Bujagali Falls disappear?'

SAQ 1.10 Bujagali pros and cons

Based on these two articles, what are the arguments for and the arguments against building a dam at Bujagali?

Activity 1.6 Bujagali Dam stakeholders

The two articles mention several different people and organisations that have an interest in the Bujagali project. Some of these stakeholders are supporters of the project and some are against. Read through the articles again and list all the stakeholders mentioned. Then group them into supporters and opposers of the planned dam.

Discussion

From the first article the stakeholders mentioned are:

Ugandan President
Ugandan Minister of Energy and Mineral Development
Aga Khan
World Bank
International Finance Corporation (IFC)
Bujagali Energy Limited (BEL)
constituent parts of BEL
local people
industry
everyone in Uganda who wants electricity.

And from the second:

Ugandan government
Ugandan Energy Minister
World Bank
local displaced families
traditional leaders
tourist service providers
guides, acrobats and swimmers
BEL officials
National Association of Professional Environmentalists (NAPE).

Understandably there is some overlap between the two articles so it makes sense to rationalise and simplify the lists. My list of stakeholders, with an indication of their position for or against the dam, is:

Ugandan government, including President and Minister – for the dam

Aga Khan – for

BEL, including its constituent parts and officials – for

World Bank – for

IFC – for

local people – this includes those who may be employed on the project as well as the displaced people, so some are for and some against

Ugandans who want electricity – for

industry – for

traditional leaders – against

people employed in tourism activities – against

NAPE – against.

To show the groups more clearly, this list can be presented as a systems map. Figure 1.26 shows my interpretation of the Bujagali stakeholders, according to the list and groups above. If you also drew a systems map it might not be quite the same but would be based on your interpretation of the articles, which may differ from mine.

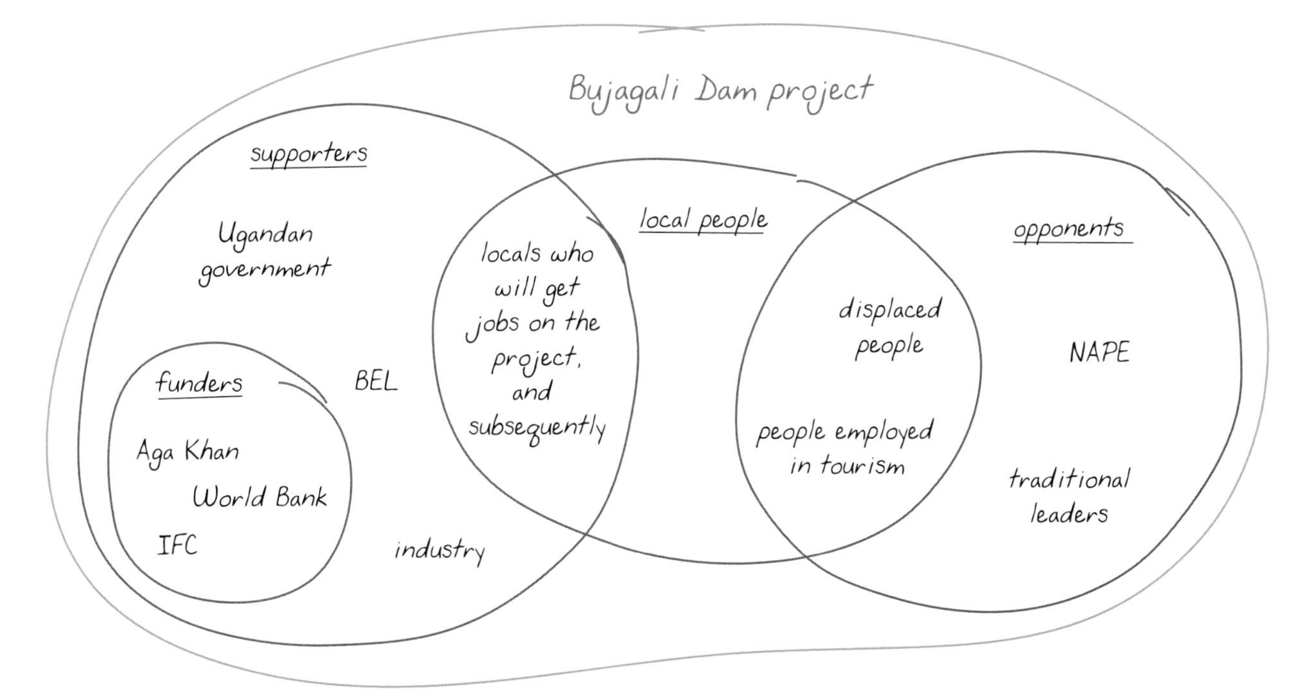

Figure 1.26 A systems map of the stakeholders in the Bujagali Dam project

6.3 Water level in Lake Victoria

One of the key issues mentioned in the *Guardian* article above (though noticeably not in the World Bank article) is the decline in the water level of Lake Victoria. Having sufficient water to power the generators is obviously critical to the potential success of the Bujagali project. Lower water levels also affect boat operators, fishermen, farmers, tourism and water supply.

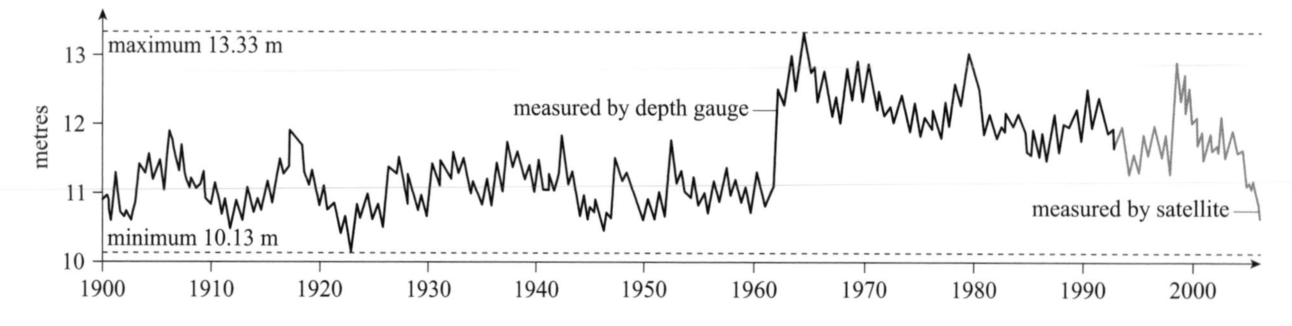

Figure 1.27 Lake Victoria water depth at Jinja, Uganda since 1900. The depth was measured by gauge until the early 1990s and by satellite since then. *(Source: adapted from Wikipedia, 2006)*

Lake Victoria has long been subject to varying water levels (Figure 1.27). There was a marked increase in depth of water in the early 1960s, which corresponded to a period of high rainfall, but the overall trend since then has been downward. Between 2003 and 2006 it fell by a record 1.2 m to the lowest level for 80 years. The reasons for this recent decline are not clear and this uncertainty is fundamental to the debate about the Bujagali dam. The *Guardian* article mentions evaporation, decreased river inflows because of lower rainfall and excessive releases through the existing power plants as possible explanations. But is this the whole story? In August 2006, Uganda's National Association of Professional Environmentalists (NAPE) organised a multi-stakeholder workshop to discuss Lake Victoria's decline. This workshop and other consultative meetings were attended by experts, Members of Parliament, civil society organisations, industry, the media, academia, researchers, community leaders, among others (NAPE, 2006). They put forward several possible factors that could have contributed to the decline of the Lake Victoria water level, including:

- drought
- over-release of water to the power stations
- wetland and forest degradation in the Lake Victoria catchment area reducing infiltration of water and increasing erosion
- evaporation as a result of increase in temperature
- climate change
- water extraction for human use
- siltation as a result of erosion of river banks and lake shoreline being used for agriculture, industry and settlement

- inappropriate policies for natural resource management and environmental planning
- inadequate knowledge and awareness of the natural resources sector
- ignoring the rights of key stakeholders in participating in decision making, especially women and youth, who are the majority
- failure to integrate indigenous knowledge and traditional conservation practices
- ever-increasing population that exerts pressure on the natural resources of the Lake Victoria basin.

The length of this list reveals some of the complexity and uncertainty surrounding the issue but, in list format, it does not reveal the possible connections between the various causes. One way to represent this more clearly is by using a ***multiple cause diagram*** (Box 1.6).

Box 1.6 Multiple cause diagrams

Multiple cause diagrams (MCDs) are what they say they are – diagrams that show the causes of something. They are used to explore why a given change, an event, or class of events, tends to occur. MCDs can clarify and explain your own, or others', understanding of a complex situation and its causes. They can sometimes reveal connections between causes that may not have occurred to you without the diagram.

To draw a multiple cause diagram, you need to follow some guidelines and conventions. MCDs are made up from phrases and arrows and follow the format shown in Figure 1.28. Each arrow carries the meaning:

[phrase at tail of arrow] causes/affects/leads to [phrase at head of arrow]

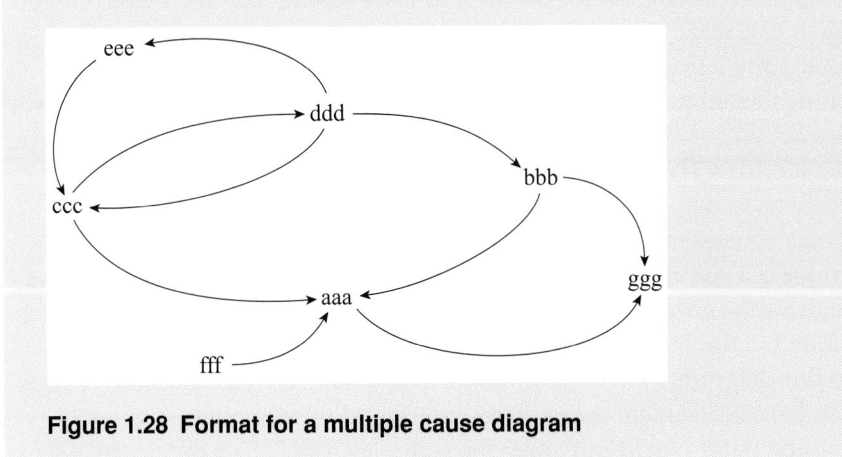

Figure 1.28 Format for a multiple cause diagram

The phrases (represented in Figure 1.28 by aaa, bbb, ccc, etc.) may be objects or events. It is best to avoid having arrows that cross over each other if at all possible. MCDs should always have a title that clearly explains what they are about.

You need to be careful to place arrows only between phrases where there is a causal connection between them. (This differs from the spray diagram technique described in Block 2 – the lines in a spray diagram indicate only a link; it does not have to be a link of any particular type.)

When drawing a MCD you normally begin with the object/event to be explained and work backwards – in other words, your starting point is actually the end point. Start by writing the object/event in the middle of a blank page.

Make a list of all the relevant factors that can cause or influence this event, either directly or indirectly. Write these on your diagram, arranged around the central event, and add linking arrows. It is usually easiest to start with direct factors before adding in the indirect causes. Some factors may act both directly and indirectly via one or more of the other causes, in which case you should use additional arrows. Expect to have to redraw your diagram – possibly more than once – in order to make it clear and to avoid crossing arrows. Often there will be loops in a MCD where item A affects item B, which affects item C, which can affect item A.

Figure 1.29 shows my version of a multiple cause diagram derived from the list above. I started this diagram by writing 'decline in Lake Victoria water level' in the middle of the page. Looking at the list, I decided that drought, excess take-off for power stations, evaporation, and extraction for human use, were direct causes so I wrote those around the centre and added arrows from them. Of the others, there appeared to be a group relating to climate so I added those next. (I started getting crossed arrows at this stage so I revised the diagram by putting drought and evaporation near to each other.) There was a group of social factors which all seemed to contribute to inappropriate policies; this was difficult to fit, but I judged that the policies must have contributed to land degradation. Population increase is a contributory cause to several of the other factors. Again, I had to redraw the diagram at this stage to avoid crossed arrows. Although included in the NAPE workshop list, I decided that siltation would not fit into this diagram. I knew that siltation could have affected the lake volume (as in Lake Nasser and Angareb reservoir) and possibly some human activities, but it would not lower the water level so I left it out. Ultimately I arrived at the diagram in Figure 1.29 and gave it the title shown in the figure caption.

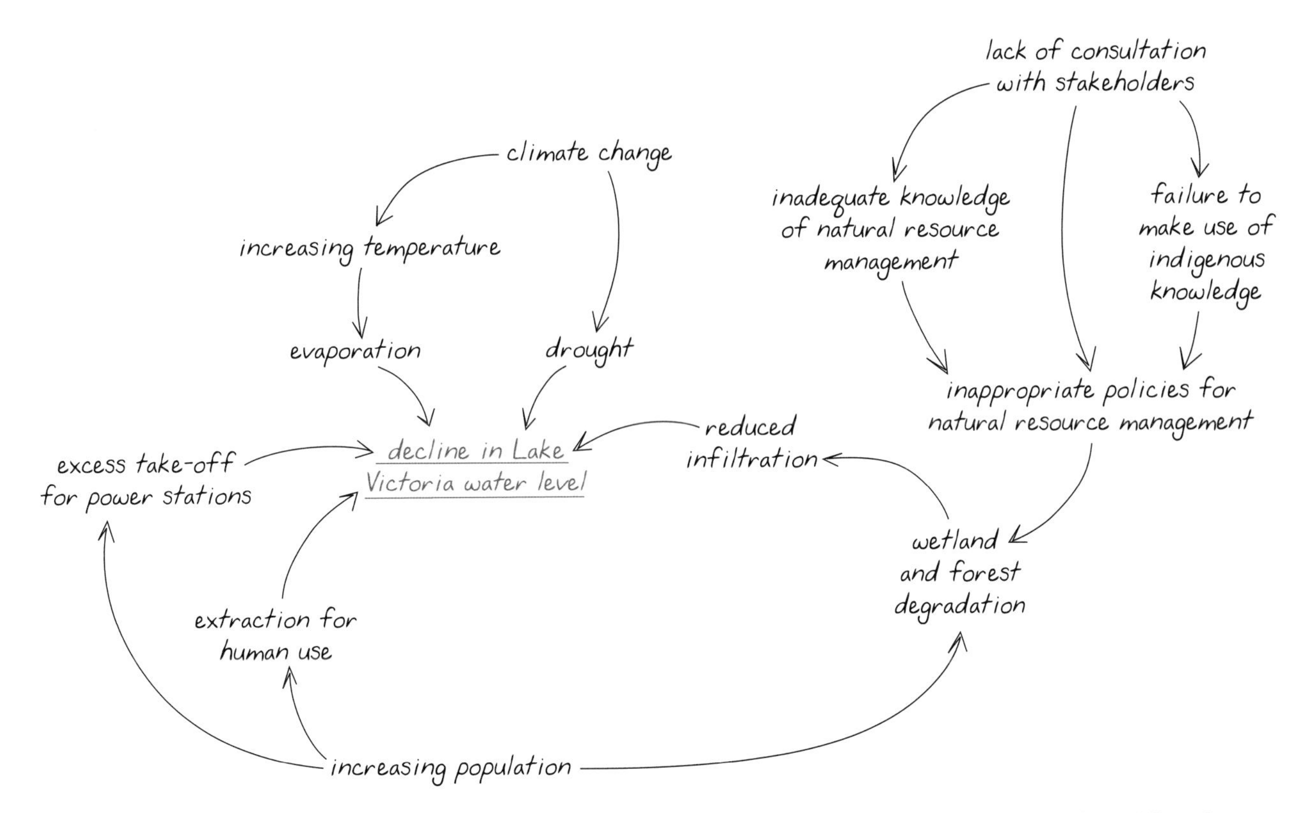

Figure 1.29 Multiple cause diagram showing possible reasons for the decline in water level in Lake Victoria, according to NAPE workshop outputs

Figure 1.29 shows that there are many different contributing causes and that several of these are interlinked. (But note that, to some extent, this is my own interpretation of the information given and so is open to question.) It also shows that some underlying indirect causes, like population increase and possible climate change, may influence several of the direct factors. Diagrams like this can be useful tools for sharing information between stakeholders as they sometimes reveal underlying links that might not be immediately obvious. What the diagram does not show is the relative importance of these different causes and, in the case of Lake Victoria, this continues to be controversial.

6.4 Alternatives to big dams

One of the main arguments used by people protesting against the Bujagali Dam and other big dam projects around the world is that there are alternatives that can achieve the same benefits. Frequently these alternatives are not given sufficient, or any, attention. They are almost invariably much smaller in scale than big dams. Some decision makers, both governments and individuals, may use major infrastructure projects like dams to demonstrate their power and authority. The possibilities of smaller, less expensive and less impressive options do not have the same appeal. This is exemplified by the quotes relating to the building of the High Aswan Dam and its role in demonstrating the importance of Egypt to the world at large. It is not possible here to explore the psychology behind decision-making processes, but it is worth bearing in mind that there are many possible underlying influences that could contribute to a decision to proceed with any development project.

At Bujagali, there are several alternatives to large-scale hydroelectric power (HEP) that NAPE and other campaigners argue should be adopted instead. These alternatives include geothermal power using hot underground reservoirs of water, which is available in Uganda. Although costly, solar power is an obvious candidate in an equatorial country. Small-scale solar power units could be installed locally and lessen the problem of lack of access to the national electricity grid. Generating electricity from municipal waste is another option and could turn an urban disposal problem into an energy-producing solution. Waste from sugar-cane processing can be turned into a clean biofuel. Uganda has a number of sugar factories, and is already producing a small amount of energy from these, but much more could be done. Smaller dams on smaller rivers for smaller HEP schemes are another option and again, local supply would help electrification in rural areas. Diversifying energy supply by adopting some of these alternatives would have the added advantage of being less risky because not all electricity supply would be dependent on the Nile alone.

As well as possible alternative energy sources, there are also different ways of achieving several of the other benefits to be gained from building a dam. Depending on the river and catchment concerned, control of flooding does not always need a dam and reservoir to hold back the water. Changing land management practices in the upper catchment can often make a big difference. For example, if forests and other vegetation have been cleared on upland slopes, this will increase the speed of run-off, reduce infiltration of water into the ground, and increase the likelihood of flooding. Trees act as a physical barrier to the rain and also use some of the water themselves, thereby decreasing the amount of surface run-off. Planting or replanting forests in upstream areas of the catchment can significantly reduce flooding further downstream. In some cases, it may be feasible to allow flooding in some places in order to protect other areas. In cases where the main purpose of a dam is irrigation, this is often used for growing crops like cotton that have high demand for water. These may have good commercial value but the embedded water within them has a cost associated with it. It may be more appropriate and more sustainable to revert to traditional crops and livelihoods that were developed in accord with local conditions. Where dams are built to ensure water supply, again there are often alternatives. Small-scale rainwater harvesting schemes at household or community level can maximise the use of water resources. ***Rainwater harvesting*** simply means collecting and storing rainwater that would otherwise run off the surface into the ground or drain. A simple garden water butt collecting rain from a roof is one example of a rainwater harvesting device, and this can be scaled up for community use (Figure 1.30). Other simple techniques include making a small depression around a new plant to hold water close to its roots.

Figure 1.30 Rainwater harvesting: the large storage tank collects rainwater from the roof which can be used by the community

Trying to weigh up the pros and cons of dams raises some very difficult questions to which there are often no easy answers. Is displacement of some people justifiable for the benefit of a larger number of others? Is the loss of tourism more or less important than more electricity? Will the dam actually provide the benefits claimed? Are the financial forecasts based on appropriate models? Are dams sustainable over a long time period?

Some of the answers depend on making accurate forecasts of future events and circumstances. These are partly dependent on the quality of data available on which to base the forecasts, data which is not always easy to obtain, and also on the competencies, perspectives and priorities of the people involved. The scope of the forecasts is also critical. Decisions to build some dams, like the High Aswan, were based on limited data and narrow perceptions. If the wider system, including all the potential problems as well as potential benefits, had been considered then possibly the decision would have been different. At Bujagali, a wider system boundary was acknowledged but the potential benefits were seen to outweigh the drawbacks. The long-term consequences and sustainability of the project are, as yet, unknown.

Summary of Section 6

There are many benefits to be gained from large dams, but they also have environmental, economic and social costs. These pros and cons can be seen in both the High Aswan Dam and Bujagali Dam projects. For many purposes, there are alternatives to big dams which would have less impact on the environment.

Two diagramming techniques have been introduced. Systems maps can be useful to define systems and their components and boundaries. Multiple cause diagrams are used to show the causal links between factors that contribute to a particular event or situation.

7 Getting enough?

The global statistics for people's access to water are alarming. According to the United Nations Development Programme (UNDP), 1.1 billion people worldwide do not have access to clean drinking water and 2.6 billion do not have access to sanitation (UNDP, 2006).

But what does this actually mean? You have seen some examples from Ethiopia but the UNDP report goes on to say:

> 'Not having access' to water and sanitation is a polite euphemism for a form of deprivation that threatens life, destroys opportunity and undermines human dignity. Being without access to water means that people resort to ditches, rivers and lakes polluted with human or animal excrement or used by animals. It also means not having sufficient water to meet even the most basic human needs.
>
> While basic needs vary, the minimum threshold is about 20 litres a day. Most of the 1.1 billion people categorised as lacking access to clean water use about 5 litres a day – one-tenth of the average daily amount used in rich countries to flush toilets. On average, people in Europe use more than 200 litres – in the United States more than 400 litres. When a European person flushes a toilet or an American person showers, he or she is using more water than is available to hundreds of millions of individuals living in urban slums or arid areas of the developing world. Dripping taps in rich countries lose more water than is available each day to more than 1 billion people.
>
> *(UNDP, 2006, pp. 5–6)*

The UNDP report focuses on people's access to water and sanitation for their own personal use but, as you have seen, that is only part of the story – the other ways of using water need to be taken into account too. A country is said to experience water scarcity when available supply is below 1000 m^3 per person per year. This is based loosely on average annual estimates of water requirements in the household, agricultural, industrial and energy sectors and, importantly, also includes the needs of the environment (Stern, 2007, p. 79). However, as noted earlier, this sort of global statistic needs to be treated with caution because it obviously varies widely depending on many factors, including local climate and land use.

7.1 Problems ...

For global water resources, the underlying problem is that there really is not that much water available to use. The water cycle provides a constantly renewing supply but large amounts of water take no active part in the cycle. Less than 1% of the total water on the Earth can be counted as part of the water cycle, in that it circulates relatively quickly. Of the rest, over 97% is in the oceans and the remainder is in polar ice sheets or trapped underground. The volume of usable water is estimated to be about 200 000 km^3 (Gleick, 2000, p. 121). It is further estimated that in the order of 4000 km^3 of this fresh water is withdrawn for human use every year and the amount is rising (Clarke and King, 2004, p. 24).

To add to the problems, the limited amount that is available is distributed very unevenly. It is unequal spatially because of the Earth's different climate zones and rainfall amounts. If you think back to Activity 1.1 on the DVD, this can be seen very clearly in the Nile basin in the contrasting rainfall received by the countries to the south, around the sources of the river, and the rainfall received in Egypt.

It is also distributed unevenly over time. The amount of available water is both seasonally variable, especially for those places with marked contrasts between the rainy season and the dry season, and annually variable as rainfall patterns may change from year to year. In addition, the uncertainty and unpredictability of future climate change not only means the possibility of more droughts, but also the possibility of more extreme rainfall events leading to soil erosion and floods.

There are also huge differences in availability of water for people depending on their economic status, as shown in the Ethiopian videos. The households that could afford it had bathrooms, or at least a clean, piped water supply, but the poor rural families only had access to a river or spring. The global crisis in water and sanitation is above all a crisis for the poor. UNDP's Human Development Report says that almost 2 in 3 people lacking access to clean water survive on less than US$2 a day, with 1 in 3 living on less than US$1 (UNDP, 2006, p. 7).

Another overarching problem is an ever-increasing population, evident both in the Nile region and worldwide. Population increase inevitably means more demands, more pressure on water supplies and more impacts from all uses – domestic, industrial and agricultural. Domestic use increases further as improved standards of living are likely to lead to increased use per person. Agricultural use increases as new areas of land are brought into production to meet rising demands for food. If the land is not entirely suitable for cultivation, this can result in other problems including land degradation by soil erosion and desertification (Box 1.7).

Box 1.7 Desertification

Desertification is the process by which formerly productive semi-arid land is degraded into unproductive desert, mainly or even solely as a result of human activities. These semi-arid areas have uncertain climate and generally sparse vegetation. The climate of semi-arid lands tends to be highly variable and rainfall is unpredictable from year to year. In years of plentiful rainfall there may be no problem, but a few years of drought will put stress on the environment. This is exacerbated by human activities, generally inappropriate agricultural activities.

These activities include ill-advised or unsustainable irrigation systems for growing crops, and cutting trees and bushes for fuelwood, but overgrazing by livestock is generally considered to be the main cause. The desertification process is a downward spiral. Vegetation cover in semi-arid areas is sparse and cannot support many grazing animals. Once the vegetation is removed the bare soil is vulnerable to erosion by wind and rain water, when it comes. The cattle add to the problem by compacting the soil so that water cannot penetrate into the ground. Surface run-off increases and reduced infiltration leads to lowering of the water table. Without groundwater the vegetation cannot re-establish and the land degenerates to desert. The problem is worsened by increasing population, which puts ever more pressure on the land and forces people to follow unsustainable agricultural methods.

The image of desertification that springs to mind is of advancing sand dunes covering everything in their path like a spreading disease. In fact, encroachment by sand is not at all typical. The symptoms of desertification are:

- reduced crop yields or crop failures in irrigated or rain-fed farmland
- loss of vegetation used for livestock grazing
- reduction in the availability of fuel wood
- reduction in fresh water for drinking.

All of these ultimately combine to result in the loss of a life-support system, not only for the people but also their animals and for wildlife. It is also important to note that lesser degrees of land degradation, not as severe as true desertification, may occur. In less arid areas, the land is better able to withstand the pressures, but overgrazing will still reduce productivity even if not causing complete degradation of the land.

SAQ 1.11 Multiple cause diagram

Using the information in Box 1.7, draw a multiple cause diagram of the causes of desertification.

Furthermore, it is not only the quantity of water that presents problems; the quality also needs to be considered. More people and more human activity will result in more waste and possible pollution, which in turn would limit availability. People are migrating to expanding cities rather than living in rural areas and this urbanisation adds to the problem by concentrating the demands and impacts in smaller localised areas.

Overall, the problem for both the world as a whole and for the Nile basin in particular is that population is increasing and water resources are finite. The resulting competition for water resources not only affects the people, but also leads to ever-increasing pressures on aquatic ecosystems and the environment as a whole.

7.2 ... and solutions?

It is not all gloom! There are some potential solutions to these problems although, it has to be said, the question mark in the heading of this section is deliberate. Few of the possible solutions are simple or easy and some have such significant problems attached to them that they may hardly be solutions at all. Some are specific to the Nile basin and others have a world-wide relevance.

One specific problem is the lack of water availability in Egypt and Sudan. Egypt is already using all its allocated amount of Nile water from the 1959 agreement and yet, with an increasing population, there will continue to be a need for more. Sudan is also using most of its permitted quantity. How can they get more water? One proposed solution is the Jonglei Canal. With echoes of the big dam stories earlier, this project exemplifies how people and the environment are in competition for the same shared resource and how this can lead to active conflict.

This plan, first proposed in 1946, involved building a canal through the Sudd wetlands in southern Sudan. In the Sudd, the river water spreads out into a vast, shallow swamp and the evaporative losses are huge. Short-circuiting the system by making the water flow in an artificial channel through the Sudd would speed its passage and reduce evaporation. The project finally got started in 1978 when work commenced on the Jonglei Canal. The canal was predicted to provide an additional 4.7 billion m^3 water per year for Egypt, which would make a significant contribution to their water needs. The consequence, however, would be to drain water out of the swamps and therefore severely damage the wetland ecosystems. The Sudd swamps are a permanent wetland area that extends and contracts each year with the annual flood. Situated within an arid region, the swamps provide water and food for many migratory animals, particularly many species of antelope and birds including the rare shoebill (Figure 1.31). They are said to be 'among the most important wetlands for birds in Africa' (Birdlife International, 2008). The people living here co-exist with the migrating herds and other wildlife. Their livelihoods are based on cattle, for which they depend on the floods to maintain the grassland, and on fishing. When the construction of the 75-metre wide canal began it split communities in two and also acted as a giant trap for game animals. The imposition of the canal by the government, based in Khartoum in the north, was deeply resented by the people of the Sudd. This, combined with several other disputes between north and south Sudan, ultimately led to the civil war that started in 1983. This bloody and bitter conflict caused the deaths of nearly 2 million civilians and devastated large areas in the south of the country. But it also brought a halt to the canal construction. By that time 260 km of the 360 km canal had been dug.

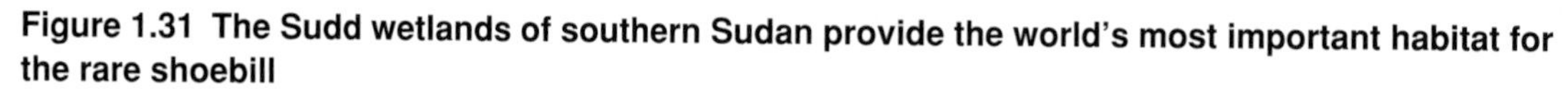

Figure 1.31 The Sudd wetlands of southern Sudan provide the world's most important habitat for the rare shoebill

Twenty-one years of war followed, during which the canal remained unfinished until a peace agreement was signed in 2005. In August 2006 it was reported that construction of the canal would recommence. There had been no consultation with local people and the announcement was met by criticism and protest. At the time of writing, in 2009, work had not started on the canal and there is no certainty that it will, but the strength of feeling reported in Sudanese newspapers and websites was such that it has been suggested that resumption of canal building could lead to a restart of the civil war (SudaneseOnline, 2006). Inevitably one has to wonder if, under these circumstances, the Jonglei Canal is really a desirable solution to the water problem for northern Sudan and Egypt after all.

On a broader note, there are several solutions that can be applied almost anywhere in the world. For piped domestic water supply, fixing leaks in the pipework is an issue that has relevance round the world. It is a particular problem in the UK because of the age of much of the water supply network, but it also has application elsewhere. Better use could be made of rainwater by employing rainwater harvesting techniques. Again this applies the world over and at a scale that almost all individuals can participate in. Recycling water that may have been used once but is still suitable for some other purposes is another way of making the most of the water available.

One technological intervention that can actually create new fresh water is desalination. Desalination is a process that converts seawater into drinking water by the removal of salt. In recent years, there have been technological advances in the industrial desalination process but it always requires specialised infrastructure and a great deal of energy, and is therefore very expensive. Usually the energy comes from oil and so it also results in significant carbon dioxide emissions. By far the largest number of desalination plants in the world is found in the oil-rich, water-poor countries of the Middle East. Seventy per cent of Saudi Arabia's fresh water is produced by desalination and it is becoming increasingly common in west and south USA, Australia and elsewhere. It can be the most viable option where other sources are problematic or overstretched and if people are willing (and able) to pay to get fresh water. Some more recent desalination proposals use solar power, wind power or biofuel to supply the required energy, reducing both costs and CO_2 emissions. The other main drawback is the highly concentrated saline water produced as effluent from the process. At coastal locations, where the majority of desalination plants are found, this is discharged to the ocean. In modest amounts and with rapid dispersal by tides and currents this may be acceptable, but the effluent can be highly polluting because the salinity exceeds the level tolerated by marine plants and animals. As global pressure on water supply increases, more and more desalination plants will be built.

For agricultural uses, there is a need for improved training and education so that farmers understand the causes of problems like salinisation and waterlogging and know how to avoid them. Strategies are needed to cope with the uncertainties of climate change and increasing unpredictability of rainfall. Farmers need to be open to different approaches. Adaptation is key in dealing with the changing circumstances. Changing farming practices by, for example, planting crops further apart so that more moisture is available for each row can help. So can growing crops that are less water dependent than some water-hungry crops, and growing different varieties that mature more quickly and so need less water.

There are also important social and institutional (and of course financial) aspects to these potential solutions. In almost all cases it is important to get support and involvement from the community involved, that is, from the stakeholders, for a project to be successful. From Activity 1.4 you may remember how the hand-dug well and pump in Abchikili village, although funded by UNICEF, was built by the people of the village and their Water Committee was responsible for managing the use and maintenance of the pump. They had a clear sense of ownership of the pump and this was an important element of its use and sustainability. The farmers interviewed in the Ethiopian river story in Activity 1.5 acted together to negotiate with other local communities and with the local irrigation authority in order to make their position heard. Cooperating and working as a group can give people a louder voice, when interacting with local and government authorities, than they would have if acting alone.

The institutional structures responsible for water management are also important. Water is frequently the responsibility of several different departments in governments or regional authorities. For example, different aspects of water management can come under the auspices of departments of agriculture, domestic supply, industry, navigation, energy, environment or health. This separates these different activities in a way that denies the processes and connections of the water cycle. ***Integrated catchment management*** offers a more systemic approach that acknowledges these links. Integrated catchment management involves both water use and land use. It recognises the connections between water quality and water quantity and those between surface and sub-surface water. Importantly, the needs of the environment are also taken into account. Of course, adopting an integrated approach to catchment management will not solve all ills and is unlikely to remove all sources of conflict and disagreement between stakeholders, but it does offer a tool to aid understanding and cooperation.

For international rivers like the Nile, there needs to be effective cooperation and treaties agreed by all countries in the basin. The establishment of the Nile Basin Commission is a positive development that will provide a forum for international discussion on how to share the Nile's resources and hopefully reduce the likelihood of conflict between the stakeholder countries. However, its forerunner, the Nile Basin Initiative, was criticised because it lacked 'neutral scientific experts' as advisors and did not have 'concrete dispute resolution provisions' (Wiebe, 2001).

Another example of international cooperation is the Nubian Sandstone Aquifer System (NSAS) outlined in Section 3.2. The Nubian Aquifer Project held its first Steering Committee meeting in December 2007. This is a joint initiative of international agencies and involves all four countries that share the aquifer: Libya, Egypt, Sudan and Chad. Its long-term goal is 'to establish a rational and equitable management of the NSAS for sustainable socio-economic development and the protection of biodiversity and land resources' (IAEA, 2008).

One question that is frequently raised in the context of conflict over water resources is the possibility of water wars. As yet, although sometimes a contributory factor in tension between neighbouring countries, no war has been caused solely by competition for water resources. There are basically two theories on this question. One is that increasing water scarcity will indeed lead to conflict between nations that share a river basin. The other is that water scarcity will encourage cooperation between countries as they have to face up to their shared responsibility to manage the water resources sustainably and equitably. In the Nile basin, internal conflict and instability in Ethiopia and Sudan in the recent past has limited their capability to embark on major water projects, but with peace settlements and the consequent rise in prosperity, these projects become more feasible. There is some irony in the fact that this internal peace could make conflict between nations over the shared water resource potentially more likely.

Climate change also brings uncertainty for the future of global water resources. In the words of the Stern report:

> Warming is very likely to intensify the water cycle, reinforcing existing patterns of scarcity and abundance and increasing the risk of droughts and floods. Rainfall is likely to increase at high latitudes, while regions with Mediterranean-like climates in both hemispheres will experience significant reductions in rainfall. Preliminary estimates suggest that the fraction of land area in extreme drought at any one time will increase from 1% to 30% by the end of this century.
>
> *(Stern, 2007, p. 3)*

But perhaps the final word should go the United Nation's Human Development Report, which says:

> With population rising and demands on the world's water expanding, so the argument runs, the future points to a 'gloomy arithmetic' of shortage. We reject this starting point. The availability of water is a concern for some countries. But the scarcity at the heart of the global water crisis is rooted in power, poverty and inequality, not in physical availability.
>
> *(UNDP, 2006, p. 2)*

Summary of Section 7

Globally, 1.1 billion people do not have access to clean drinking water. The quantity of available water is limited and unevenly distributed. Population increase brings increasing demand for water resources. There are possible solutions to some of the problems but many of these have drawbacks too.

Summary of Part 1

Part 1 of Block 3 has discussed water resources in the Nile basin and considered the connections between water, people and environment. Section 1 introduced the Nile basin and our use of water at home. Section 2 described some of the historical background that still influences water use in the Nile basin to this day. In Section 3 the water cycle was described, the significance of water quantity and quality was discussed and some systems ideas were introduced. Section 4 considered some of the different technologies involved in water supply and Section 5 described the many ways humans make use of water. Dams and their impacts were the focus of Section 6. Section 7 summarised some of the issues surrounding the provision of water to a growing population by sustainable means.

After completing Part 1 you should be able to:

- describe the water cycle
- discuss the many ways in which humans make use of water and how these uses may compete with each other
- appreciate the need for sustainable use of water and some of the ways this can be achieved
- appreciate the complexities of natural resource management and the need to consider all stakeholders
- describe some of the benefits of large dams and their social and environmental impacts
- recognise the value of a systems approach and the need to consider boundaries, system components and interactions
- draw a multiple cause diagram.

Answers to SAQs

SAQ 1.1

The three countries occupying the largest proportion of the Nile basin are Sudan, Ethiopia and Egypt According to the Table in Activity 1.1. Sudan has 63.6% of the basin area, Ethiopia 11.7% and Egypt 10.5%. The other countries each occupy less than 10% of the basin area.

In general terms, the north of the Nile basin has very little rain in comparison with the south. From the rainfall map in Activity 1.1, Egypt and the north of Sudan have less than 25 mm per year of rain, whereas the parts of Ethiopia that lie within the basin, Uganda and other southern parts of the basin have more than 600 mm per year.

SAQ 1.2

Fish are similar to soil and forest, i.e. renewable but susceptible to human modification.

Fish stocks will replace themselves, though this will take time for the fish to breed and reach maturity. However, if fisheries are overexploited, i.e. fish are removed at too high a rate or removed before they have matured, then the stocks will cease to be fully replaced.

SAQ 1.3

The first step is to convert the volume of the aquifer, which is given in cubic kilometres (15 000 km^3) into the same units as the quoted rate of daily extraction. This is given in millions of cubic metres (6.5 million m^3) which can also be written as 6.5×10^6 m^3.

There are 1000 m in 1 km and 10^9 m^3 in 1 km^3 ($10^9 = 1000 \times 1000 \times 1000$)

therefore 15 000 km^3 = $15\,000 \times 10^9$ m^3.

Water is extracted at 6.5 million m^3 per day = 6.5×10^6 m^3 per day.

Number of days that reserve will last is:

$$\frac{15\,000 \times 10^{\not{9}\,3}}{6.5 \times \not{10^6}}$$

$$= \frac{15\,000 \times 10^3}{6.5}$$

$= 2308 \times 10^3$ days.

Divided by 365,

= 6323 years

which can be rounded down to 6000 years.

6000 years is a long time. I think I would probably describe this as sustainable use in that the supply would last for a great many future generations. However, fossil water is a non-renewable resource and so will ultimately run out; therefore it cannot be sustainable in perpetuity. But there are other factors to consider. It should be noted that this calculation is based on the current estimate of the size of the recoverable reserve. It is possible that this volume will increase if new extraction techniques and higher economic value lead to more of the 500 000 km^3 that is believed to exist becoming usable. Also, although this estimate is based on scientific assessment techniques it has been acknowledged that there are gaps in the hydrological and geological knowledge of the NSAS (IAEA, 2008). As with many scientific measurements, there has to be some uncertainty about this data, especially if you consider the difficulties of measuring the capacity of an aquifer.

If you were puzzled by the mathematics in this SAQ or found it difficult to follow the calculation, there will be more on calculating with powers of ten in Block 4.

SAQ 1.4

Respiration (as in Block 1 Figure 2.10 The basic carbon cycle) is a process that converts starting materials of carbohydrates and oxygen into products of carbon dioxide and water.

Note that carbohydrates are a form of organic matter. The micro-organisms in water that need oxygen to respire as they consume organic matter are performing a similar function to soil micro-organisms, as described in Block 1 Section 3.3.1.

SAQ 1.5

Yeshiemebet got her water from an unprotected natural spring emerging from the rocks. Mulugojam had a tap within the compound in which she lived, which was supplied by a piped supply of treated water from a protected spring some distance away.

The unprotected spring water comes from groundwater reserves, so potential sources of pollution would include any substances that might have infiltrated into the groundwater from the surface. The video did not show details of possible sources of pollution but it is possible to speculate that this might include animal wastes, human wastes or agricultural chemicals such as fertilisers. The water from the tap is piped from a protected source, which brings some assurance of good quality and should be protected from pollution. Problems might possibly include some failure in the system such as a break in the supply pipe or perhaps a problem in the treatment process. As in the first case, contamination from polluted water infiltrating into the ground from the surrounding catchment area could also be a problem.

SAQ 1.6

Egypt and Sudan use most water, both in total and per person, significantly more water than any other Nile country (though nowhere near as much as the USA).

Both Egypt and Sudan use very large quantities of water for agricultural purposes, i.e. irrigation. Low rainfall and high temperatures that increase evaporation make Egypt and Sudan very dependent on water from rivers and groundwater for this purpose. Upstream countries of the Nile generally have more rainfall.

SAQ 1.7

From Table 1.1, the estimated withdrawal in the UK for 2000 was 201 m^3 per person per year. The question asks for the answer in litres per person per day.

Given that 1 m^3 is 1000 litres:

water withdrawal in the UK

$$= \frac{201 \times 1000}{365}$$

$=$ 550 litres per person per day.

The figure of 50 litres per person per day is an estimate of the water required specifically for domestic needs, but the data in Table 1.1 includes industrial and agricultural, as well as domestic use. The total withdrawn for all these purposes has been divided by the population to arrive at a figure of withdrawal per person. Inevitably this is much greater than an individual's domestic use.

Another reason for the difference is that 50 litres per person per day refers to the needs of people anywhere the world. It is about human requirement for water, not UK use. The two figures are estimates of two different things so there is no particular reason why they should be the same.

Although the question asks about water withdrawal, you could use the Table 1.1 data to compare just UK domestic use with the 50 litres figure. Table 1.1 states that domestic use in the UK is 20% of the total; 20% of 550 litres is 110 litres per person per day for UK domestic use. This excludes industrial and agricultural use but is still roughly twice the basic water requirement for personal human needs.

SAQ 1.8

The stated reasons for building the High Aswan Dam were to even out seasonal fluctuations in flow, for irrigation and for power generation, but national pride was also involved. Political and national aims dominated over the stated reasons to the extent that the investigation of the true costs and benefits of building the dam was very limited. The global political context at the time was competition and hostility between the Soviet Union and Western powers. The dam was built with Soviet support and became a symbol of national status and independence. It was one of the contributory causes of the Suez crisis. (102 words)

SAQ 1.9

Benefits: irrigation; flood control; electricity; fishery in Lake Nasser; improved navigation below the dam.

Less desirable consequences: displacement of local people; sediment deposited in the lake, decreasing its capacity; sediment lost from the flood plain and the need for increased artificial fertiliser; loss of sediment from the delta and consequent erosion; scouring of the river course; increased salinisation and waterlogging; increased schistosomiasis infection; damage to fisheries in the Mediterranean; poorer water quality in cities, necessitating more chlorination. You might also include water loss by evaporation from the lake but without the dam, most of the 'lost' water would otherwise presumably have flowed out into the sea so would have been 'lost' to Egypt by other means.

SAQ 1.10

Arguments for the dam: electricity generated by the power plant will create employment opportunities, and aid industry and development in general. It is a run-of-river project and will reuse water previously used by two upstream power plants so will not create a huge reservoir with its attendant environmental impacts.

Arguments against: doubts over the accuracy of the forecast energy it will provide; uncertainty over Lake Victoria levels, which could reduce its effectiveness; alternative sources of energy could be more appropriate; the network for distributing electricity through the country is incomplete; it will have a significant damaging impact on tourism and associated livelihoods; impact on local communities who will be displaced by the development project.

SAQ 1.11

Firstly, I re-read the box and drew up a list of the factors that contribute to desertification. Then I tried to decide if they are direct or indirect causes.

My list, in the order they are mentioned, is: human activities; drought; inappropriate agricultural activities subdivided into unsustainable irrigation systems and overgrazing by cattle; removal of vegetation; soil erosion; soil compaction by cattle; poor penetration of water into the ground; increased surface run-off; lowering of water table; poor regeneration of vegetation; increasing population.

Your diagram should look something like Figure 1.32.

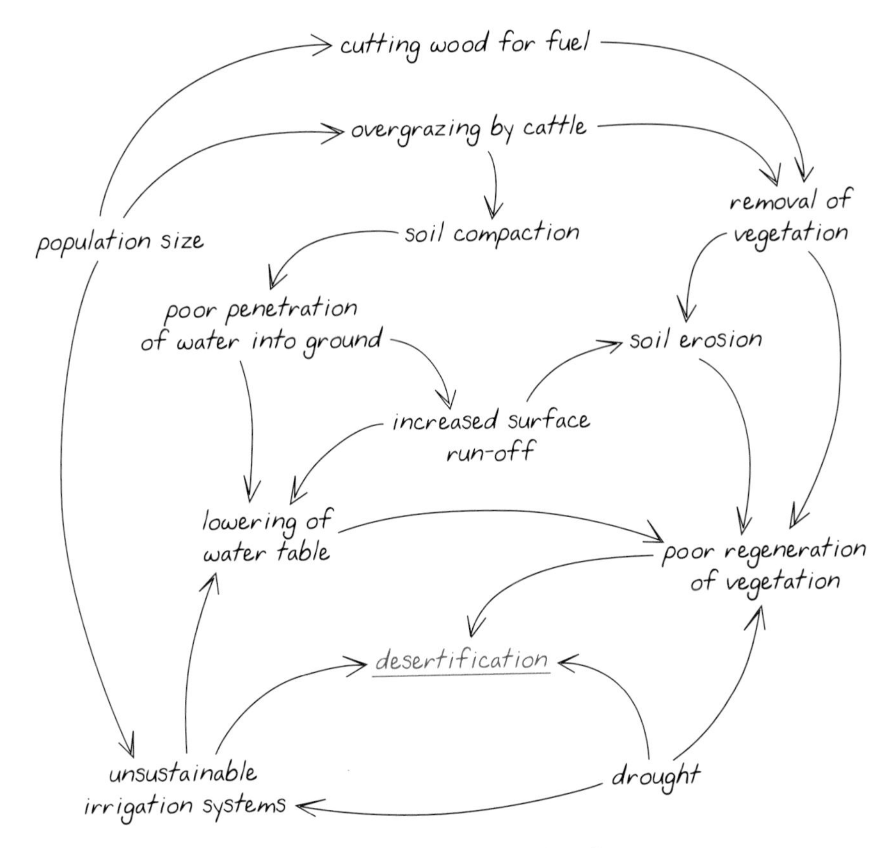

Figure 1.32 Multiple cause diagram of desertification

References

Birdlife International (2008) *Sudd (Bahr-el-Jebel System)*, Birdlife IBA Factsheet SD014, http://www.birdlife.org.datazone/sites/index.html (Accessed 14 September 2008).

Clarke, R. and King, J. (2004) *The Atlas of Water*, London, Earthscan.

Collins, R. O. (2003) *The Inscrutable Nile at the beginning of the new Millennium*, unpublished paper, University of California Santa Barbara, available from http://www.history.ucsb.edu/faculty/Inscrutable%20Nile1.pdf, p. 1 (Accessed 10 July 2008).

El-Ashry, M. T. (1993) 'Policies for water resources management in arid and semi-arid regions', p. 51 in Biswas, A. K., Jellali, M. and Stout, G. E. (eds) (1993) *Water for Sustainable Development in the Twenty-first Century*, Delhi, Oxford University Press.

Gleick, P. H. (2000) *The World's Water 2000–2001*, Washington DC, Island Press.

Howell, P. and Allan, J. A. (1994) *The Nile: sharing a scarce resource*, Cambridge, Cambridge University Press.

IAEA (International Atomic Energy Authority) (2007) *Nubian Sandstone Aquifer System (NSAS) Technical Baseline Meeting Report*, May 2006, IAEA RAF/8/036, http://www-naweb.iaea.org/napc/ih/Nubian/IHS_nubian.html (Accessed 28 October 2008).

IAEA (International Atomic Energy Authority) (2008) *Nubian Aquifer Project*, http://www-naweb.iaea.org/napc/ih/Nubian/IHS_nubian_project_summary.html (Accessed 28 October 2008).

Kagwanja, P. (2007) 'Calming the Waters: The East African Community and Conflict over the Nile Resources', *Journal of Eastern African Studies*, vol. 1 no. 3, pp. 321–37.

Mather, A. S. and Chapman, K. (1995) *Environmental Resources*, Harlow, Longman.

McCully, P. (1996) *Silenced Rivers: the Ecology and Politics of Large Dams*, London, Zed Books.

Merriam-Webster Online (2009) 'Technology', *Merriam-Webster Online Dictionary*, http://www.merriam-webster.com/dictionary/technology (Accessed 5 March 2009).

Metawie, A. (2004) 'History of cooperation in the Nile basin', *International Journal of Water Resources Development*, vol. 20, no. 3, pp. 47–63.

Mukyala, E. (2008) *Nile Perch, Tilapia fish diminishing*, The New Vision, http://www.newvision.co.ug/PA/8/17/637806 (Accessed 11 September 2008).

NAPE (2006) *Multi-stakeholder Consultations on the Lake Victoria Crisis and Strategy for the Next Steps*, www.nape.org.ug (Accessed 10 July 2008).

NBI (Nile Basin Initiative) (2009) *NBI Background,* http://www.nilebasin.org/index.php?option=com_content&task=view&id=13&Itemid=42) (Accessed 5 March 2009).

O'Riordan, T. and More, R. J. (1969) 'Choice in water use', p. 194 in Chorley, R. J. (ed) (1969) *Introduction to Geographical Hydrology*, London, Methuen.

Rice, X. (2007) 'White water torrent to die as nation gambles on huge Nile dam project', 31 May, http://www.guardian.co.uk/environment/2007/may/31/energy.uganda (Accessed 28 January 2009).

Rycroft, R. and Szyliowicz, J. (1980) 'The Technological Dimension of Decision Making: The Case of the Aswan High Dam', *World Politics*, vol. 33, no. 1, pp. 48–9.

Stern, N. (2007) *The Economics of Climate Change: The Stern Review*, Cambridge, Cambridge University Press.

SudaneseOnline (2006) *A Call for Southern Mass to Condemn the Digging of the Jonglei Canal*, http://www.sudaneseonline.com/en/article_2176.shtml (Accessed 11 September 2008).

Timmerman, J. G. (2005) *Transboundary River Basin Management Regimes: the Nile Basin Case Study*. Background report to Deliverable 1.3.1 of the NeWater project, Lelystad.

UNDP (2006) *Human Development Report 2006, Beyond scarcity: power, poverty and the global water crisis*, United Nations Development Programme, Basingstoke, Palgrave Macmillan.

UNESCO (2006) *2nd UN World Water Development Report: Water, a shared responsibility*, http://www.unesco.org/water/wwap/wwdr/wwdr2 (Accessed 28 October 2008).

de Villiers, M. (1999) *Water Wars: Is the world's water runnin*g out?, London, Weidenfeld & Nicolson, p. 242.

Walsh, C. M. and Shalita S. (2007) 'Uganda's President and the Aga Khan cut ribbon on Bujagali Dam Project', 21 August, http://web.worldbank.org/WBSITE/EXTERNAL/COUNTRIES/AFRICAEXT/0,,contentMDK:21450929 ~menuPK:258659~pagePK:2865106 ~piPK:2865128~theSitePK:258644,00.html (Accessed 28 January 2009).

Waterbury, J. (1979) *The Hydropolitics of the Nile Valley*, New York, Syracuse University Press.

Water UK (2008) *Ask About: Adults*, http://www.water.org.uk/home/water-for-health/medical-facts/adults, (Accessed 5 March 2009).

Waterwise (2007) *Hidden Waters: A Waterwise Briefing*, February 2007, http://www.waterwise.org.uk/reducing_water_wastage_in_the_uk/the_facts (Accessed November 2008).

Wiebe, K. (2001) 'The Nile River: Potential for conflict and cooperation in the face of water degradation', *Natural Resources Journal*, vol. 41, no. 3, pp. 731–54.

Wikipedia (2006) 'File:Hydrography-graph-Lake Victoria.svg', http://en.wikipedia.org/wiki/File:Hydrography-graph-Lake_Victoria.svg (Accessed 28 January 2009).

World Bank (n.d.) 'NBI Overview', http://go.worldbank.org/1J4ISEE170 (Accessed 27 April 2009).

World Resources Institute (n.d.) 'A10 Nile: watersheds of Africa', http://multimedia.wri.org/watersheds_2003/af15.html (Accessed 27 April 2009).

Part 2

The forest is ours!

Susan Fawssett

Introduction 1

You will probably be familiar with the depiction of nature in various natural history documentaries. Although predation, starvation and survival are often shown quite realistically, the stories are woven together through beautiful and imaginative filming. But what is striking is that there are generally very few people presented in these films. In such films, 'nature' is almost seen as the antithesis of humanity, perhaps a relic of the unfortunate human–environment divide discussed in Block 1.

This part of the course seeks to put people back into the picture, and to investigate the impact they have. In particular, I will explore human–wildlife conflict, which arises when the needs and interests of humans encroach on and damage wildlife and the habitats upon which it depends. I will examine some of the roots and dimensions of human–wildlife conflict and consider how policies to address it have emerged. This will be done through the lens of conservation policy. I argue that conservation is not simply something that is done to an environment, but instead is a dynamic process of change involving social and natural dimensions. It is also inherently political, involving different groups of people with different views and perspectives and unequal power relations. Thus, I will look at how human–wildlife conflict is produced, shaped, represented and addressed.

In studying this part, you will also develop your skills in critically reading a range of texts (book extracts, journal articles and unpublished documents), engage with a diverse range of resources (audio-visual, maps and photos) in order to integrate and build a picture of what is happening, and move towards critically looking at how conservation is done today. When you have a good understanding of the different pressures at play in conservation you will be asked to step into the shoes of a wildlife manager and make a real conservation recommendation yourself.

This part is different from other parts in the course because you will be studying much of it on the course DVD. The case study of the mountain gorillas of Bwindi Impenetrable National Park in Uganda has spectacular visual content. What links this part to Part 1 is that it also focuses on conflict and cooperation, but in one specific corner of the Nile basin. It looks at an iconic species, the mountain gorilla, and the conflicts between the desire to conserve them and the needs of the local people to use the resources of the forest where the gorillas live. This conflict has been negotiated, leading to a cooperative approach to forest management. I consider how this was achieved by deploying an analytical approach you were first introduced to in Part 1, namely stakeholder analysis. So there is much continuity with Part 1, although rather than looking at the resource of water, here I look at wildlife.

2 A place for wildlife

In 2008, the human population of the world stood at 6.7 billion, and is expected to expand to 9 billion over the next 40 years. A growing population leads to pressures on environments, as the needs of an expanding human population reduce both the areas available for other species and total biodiversity. However, our demands for natural resources are expanding even faster than human population numbers. As heavily populated countries like China and India develop, their consumption increases. Changing settlement patterns mean that half the world's people now live in urban areas. In the early stages of development urban dwellers often consume more than rural dwellers as a result of their increased purchasing power. This places a strain on resources, including water, as we saw in Part 1. Climate change places a further pressure on habitats as landforms are changed by extreme weather events and animals and people sometimes migrate in search of more hospitable conditions. The result is that people and wildlife are coming into frequent contact with each other and increasingly competing for land, food and water.

Such competition for resources has led to some species being threatened or lost. While there is always a natural level of species loss and new species being discovered, the actual level of loss is believed to be much higher than it would be in the absence of human activity, some putting the level of species loss at 150 each day (Sigmar, 2007). This loss of biodiversity is considered by some scientists as the second most important global threat to humans after climate change (you might like to look back at Block 1 Part 3 to remind yourself about biodiversity). Biodiversity is important because it indirectly and directly sustains us, humans. It provides our food, fuel, pharmaceuticals, shelter, purifies our air and water, decomposes our waste and moderates our planet's climate. Biodiversity loss threatens to upset the current form of life on which we rely. The International Union for Conservation of Nature (IUCN) is the world's oldest and largest environmental network and consists of governments, NGOs and scientists in more than 160 countries. It works to conserve the diversity of nature and supports policies that use natural resources in an equitable and sustainable way. It monitors globally threatened species through its Red List, where threatened species are classified either as endangered, when they number in their thousands, or critically endangered, when they number in their hundreds.

The IUCN works with and advises governments on biodiversity issues. This feeds into individual governments' national policies on conservation and biodiversity. As an example, Figure 2.1 shows the UK Government's conservation and biodiversity policy document.

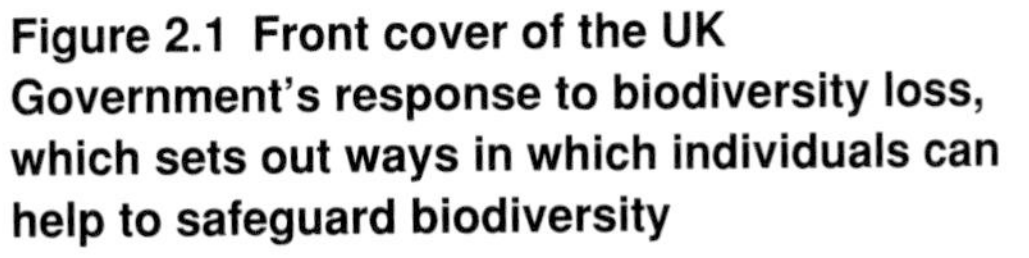

Figure 2.1 Front cover of the UK Government's response to biodiversity loss, which sets out ways in which individuals can help to safeguard biodiversity

Study note: acronyms

There are a lot of acronyms in this part: NGO and IUCN are two examples. It might be a good idea for you to compile your own checklist of what they stand for, and their function, so you don't have to keep checking back. This can be a useful part of active learning. This can be your own personal glossary, even though the course has one. There is a lot to be said for putting things in your own words.

The IUCN works to support biodiversity with governments, civil societies and the private sector by assisting in the planning, implementation, monitoring and evaluation of conservation work around the globe. But what is meant by conservation, why do it and how is it done?

2.1 What is conservation?

I imagine that in thinking about conservation you think about preserving attractive or important plants and animals. As such, you are considering the 'what' of conservation; what is conserved. However, there is an important difference between preserving our environment and conserving it. When I preserve something I try to keep it as it is and protect it from change. In contrast, when I conserve something I recognise that change is inevitable but try to retain its essential characteristics and keep it from harm. Here are some definitions of conservation:

- Conservation is the protection of wilderness for its beauty.
- Conservation is the protection of resources to provide for sustainable livelihoods.
- Conservation is the protection of species to maintain biodiversity.

There are some fundamental differences between these definitions. They have different emphases, which reflects the fact that conservation is a contested concept. By this I mean that not everyone thinks about conservation in the same way. The first definition seeks to protect wilderness (in the sense of areas or species that are not specifically used by humans) because it is perceived by humans to be beautiful. It is protected even though it is seen as having no practical utility for humans; we cannot use it for our basic needs. As such, it has an intrinsic, non-use or ***non-instrumental value***.

Biophysical environment: as noted in Block 1, Part 1, humans should not be considered as separate from our environment. 'Biophysical environment' is used here for the biological and physical elements of our environment, it includes the links between humans and their surroundings, but excludes social and economic relationships.

The second definition places a use value on our biophysical environment, as it is a resource that can be exploited by humans. In this case our environment holds a pool of resources that humans can use to live. As such, our environment has ***instrumental value***.

The third definition is a hybrid of the two previous definitions; it recognises non-instrumental value in different species, but also instrumental value in protecting species for the maintenance of biodiversity which is useful for humans.

2.2 Why conserve our biophysical environment?

I have commented on the importance of biodiversity for our lives. But beyond this, why is it important to think about our biophysical environment in these two different ways, non-instrumental and instrumental? I think it is important because the former can act as a check or constraint on the latter. By recognising that our environment has intrinsic or non-instrumental value we place a certain premium on it. This premium is set against our need to exploit our environment for our own ends. It is this tension between non-instrumental and instrumental value that is played out in the debate that underpins conservation, and indeed, this course.

Activity 2.1 Instrumental and non-instrumental value

Classify the following 'things' as having either non-instrumental or instrumental value.

- pet dog
- litre of engine oil
- hammer
- recording of Beethoven's 5th Symphony
- dress
- landscape painting
- sandwich.

Discussion

Instrumental value: litre of engine oil, sandwich, dress, hammer.

Non-instrumental value: recording of Beethoven's 5th symphony, pet dog, landscape painting.

Did you find this activity quite straightforward? I thought it was until, on closer reflection, I realised that a few of the 'things' were not so easy to classify. For example, I categorised the painting as having non-instrumental value, but for the artist who sells it to make a living, and perhaps the collector who buys it as an investment, it has instrumental value. Another example from the list above is the dress, which has instrumental value in providing a covering and warmth, and non-instrumental value in being a statement of fashion, taste and perhaps wealth if it carries an expensive designer label.

I think there is also something intellectually and emotionally rewarding about valuing something for its non-instrumental value. It introduces a certain desired balance to my personality. I like to think I am more than the sum of my needs. Moreover, possibly seeing both instrumental and non-instrumental value together encourages me to use resources more sparingly and carefully than I might otherwise do, and encourages me, as a member of the dominant species on Earth, to develop a ***duty of care*** for the environment, by which I mean taking some responsibility for the protection of the environment or exercising stewardship. After all, humans are the species that has wrought greatest change to our planet.

I hope I don't sound too evangelical. It is important to recognise that our biophysical environment is not something 'out there', having an untouchable, objective reality, but is thought about and presented by different groups in different ways, as mentioned in the Introduction to this block. This is because the way we think about our environment or its representation is conditioned by social, economic and political factors. For example, as you read in Block 2, the Inuit and the city dweller think quite differently about the polar bear.

Although both show it respect, they do it in different ways: one occasionally kills it for survival while the other campaigns to protect it as a threatened species. How the requirements of species other than humans are given form and value alongside human needs and wants varies in different places and at different times. Conservation is a key approach today because of the value we place on biodiversity, but this is a process of adaptation, as I will show in the next section.

So having looked at the 'what' and 'why' of conservation, attention now needs to be turned to the 'how'.

2.3 How is conservation done?

Conservation of our biophysical environment is not static, but changes over time and space. In Britain, conservation has a long history, with the English kings of the Middle Ages protecting great tranches of countryside as their private hunting grounds (Figure 2.2). Indeed, the word 'wilderness' comes from an Old English word, which meant 'the place of wild deer'. Protection for the purposes of hunting does not accord with any of my three definitions of conservation, but areas protected for hunting are valuable conservation areas for all wildlife, not just the target species, albeit coincidental and an added bonus. Britain took its approach to conservation with it as part of Empire, and as the British Empire in Africa approached its end, the colonial administrators set up game reserves to protect the 'big game' they had so enjoyed, leaving an enduring legacy of colonial rule (BC Spaces, 2008).

Figure 2.2 ***A Stag Hunt in a Forest*, oil painting by Jan Hackaert and Nicolaes Berchem, painted about 1660** *(Source: National Gallery)*

In a huge country like the USA, conservation has focused on wilderness areas, with the first National Park, Yellowstone, founded in 1872 (Figure 2.3). Towards the end of the nineteenth century, when 'the frontier' of America no longer seemed infinite, Yellowstone was meant to protect parkland and capture the essence of what it was to be American. Identity was rooted in having a special relationship with wilderness. The park offered pristine wilderness by protecting it from human interference (BC Spaces, 2008).

Figure 2.3 Yellowstone National Park, USA

What these early British and American approaches to conservation have in common is a particular attitude to local people. Essentially, the presence of people living in the conserved or protected areas was perceived as incompatible with their protected status. It was felt that people threatened the state of the protected area. This often led to the people being forcibly evicted from the area and denied access to the resources – land, water and wildlife – they had previously enjoyed. This attitude to local people proved very enduring. In the last quarter of the twentieth century, when conservation policy became a subject of academic and political interest, this approach became known as ***fortress conservation***.

Fortress conservation started from the premise that the protected area was under siege by local people and their destructive habits. It characterised hunting as 'poaching', and argued that the protected areas needed defending. Fences were needed to keep people out and law enforcement through fines imposed if they 'trespassed'. Thus, local people were criminalised by the adoption of a fortress approach. They were marginalised in not being consulted. And they were made poorer as they lost access to activities to maintain livelihoods (Siurua, 2006, pp.74–5).

Fortress conservation found expression as a conservation approach around the world.

B. N. Upreti of the Nepal Environmental Conservation Group describes these processes in Nepal in the following way:

> Prior to the establishment of parks and reserves, local people were free to collect fuelwood, timber, fodder and thatch grass from the forest. Local people were dependent upon it for grazing and fodder for their livestock, bamboo and medicinal herbs for their livelihood and fishing and hunting for a major source of protein.
>
> With the declaration of parks and reserves in such areas many people have been legally restrained from using their traditional rights to these resources. Those people living outside the boundaries have no legal recourse to procure compensation for their lost benefits. They ask themselves why they have been deprived of this inexhaustible natural resource which is a common property of the community. They think that it is unjust that 'outsiders' impose these restrictions and they express their feelings of discontent in various ways. Their reactions are revealed by not obeying the park regulations and by engaging themselves in prohibited activities such as grazing animals and smuggling firewood, timber and grass from within the boundaries, particularly in Terai areas. To demonstrate their anger they sometimes vandalise park property by damaging bridges, signposts and boundary pillars.
>
> *(Siurua, 2006, pp. 74–5)*

Fortress conservation found further expression in Africa in the work of Dian Fossey, who was dedicated to protecting the mountain gorillas of the Virunga mountain range in Rwanda (Figure 2.4). Fossey studied the mountain gorillas in the 1970s and 1980s from her base at Karisoke. You may have seen the film *Gorillas in the Mist*, starring Sigourney Weaver as Fossey, which is based on her book of the same name. Fossey used the term 'active conservation' to refer to fortress conservation.

Figure 2.4 Dian Fossey with one of the mountain gorillas she studied at Karisoke

Activity 2.2 Dian Fossey and fortress conservation

Read the following extract from Dian Fossey's book, *Gorillas in the Mist*, where she explains how she implemented a fortress conservation approach, although she calls her approach 'active conservation'. Jot down a few notes to answer these two questions:

What is her attitude to the local people?

Do you feel her view is justified?

> … hundreds of antipoacher patrols have set out from Karisoke into the heartland of the Virungas to cut traps, confiscate encroachers' weapons, and release newly trapped animals from snares. Active conservation within a steadily shrinking internationally designated sanctuary filled with poachers, traps, herdsmen, farmers, and beekeepers needs to be supplemented by Rwandese and Zaioirese enforcement of anti-encroacher laws as well as severe penalties for the illegal sale of poached animals for their meat, skins, tusks, or for financial profits.
>
> *(Fossey, 1983, pp. 57–8)*

Zaioirese: the people of Zaire. Zaire was the previous name of the Democratic Republic of Congo, commonly referred to as DRC.

Discussion

Fossey groups herders, farmers and beekeepers together with poachers and their traps, suggesting that she sees little or no difference between them – or perhaps that it is the same people who are both poachers *and* herdsmen, farmers, etc. It's not possible to tell if that is a fair assessment but she clearly wants to keep all people out of the forest regardless of whether their needs are legal and legitimate or not.

Only you know if you think her view was justified, but I felt somewhat uneasy with Fossey's apparent attitude to the local people. Her emphasis on patrols, laws and penalties perhaps seems rather insensitive to the peoples' needs from the forest. In this brief extract you can see how they are criminalised and demonised for using a resource that has traditionally been available to them. Indeed, Fossey's uncompromising approach may have led to her murder in 1985.

Wider resistance to fortress conservation grew for a number of reasons. Firstly, local people began to contest their exclusion from protected areas. Their exclusion from ancestral lands and so the means to make a livelihood, led to greater impoverishment; the people began to resist park authorities and break park regulations. Having had little involvement in the decision to exclude them or an explanation of the conservation reasons that underpinned it, they felt that wildlife was valued more than people (Siurua, 2006).

Secondly, the assumption that underpinned fortress conservation was that local peoples' use of the forest ecosystem threatened it and was unsustainable. But local people had lived alongside other species in the seized lands for generations. They held much practical and detailed knowledge about how to use the forest's resources sustainably and this was not being tapped.

Thirdly, the ethical position of excluding local people in order to protect areas for a predominantly Western, conservation-minded world began to be challenged by concerned groups. Was it right to exclude people from a traditional livelihood resource in order to safeguard that same resource for foreigners? Local peoples' exclusion and their criminalisation was seen as imposed by outsiders, both national government elites who introduced protected area status and foreign conservationists.

Fourthly, the lack of success of fortress conservation generated a search for alternatives. It had not prevented the destruction of valued ecosystems as habitat degradation and species loss continued. The threats to biodiversity were growing rather than diminishing. Fortress conservation was not preserving the protected areas in the way expected.

Resistance to and disillusionment with fortress conservation led to a search for new approaches to conservation. At the same time, new approaches were also being tried by development NGOs attempting to build the livelihoods of poor people around the world. By the late 1980s and early 1990s development was being seen by some as not so much about economic growth but more about empowering local people to find their own solutions to their problems. Such people-centred strategies were called 'bottom up', which meant giving local people a voice, listening to them, and valuing their local knowledge. This was in contrast to earlier approaches, which had been 'top down', where local people were told what was best for them and their own knowledge was not valued. At the interface with conservation, this meant engaging local people in managing the protected areas and helping them derive benefits from involvement. It was hoped that they would then develop an interest in the success of the policy. As Brian Child, a southern African wildlife manager and university professor argued, the 'real threat to wildlife is poverty, not poaching' (Siurua, 2006, p. 76).

> The problem was beginning to be thought about, or constructed differently. Biodiversity conservation began to be seen as depending in large measure on the ways in which local people were brought into the management of the protected area. A search began for the best strategies and approaches for incorporating local communities in the process which continues today. Thus a more inclusive and holistic approach to conservation began to emerge. It became known as 'community conservation' or integrated conservation and development (ICD). At its core was the belief that conservation of land and wildlife could best be achieved by working with the local people both to understand the non-instrumental value of the protected areas (their innate beauty), and to help establish alternative livelihoods as a substitute for the loss of instrumental value from access to the protected area. Moreover, the local people bear the costs in loss of access, so should share in the benefits of conservation. Thus, the approach has been from preservation to sustainable, managed use.
>
> *(Child, 1993)*

ICD: Integrated Conservation and Development

Local peoples' knowledge and their management of the biophysical environment became more important in attitudes towards conservation. Conservation was being constructed differently. The dichotomy between humanity and the biophysical environment that was enshrined in fortress conservation was breaking down, and new policies recognised that effective conservation had to be built by integrating social and ecological processes. There was a growing recognition that these were complementary and tightly linked and needed the ICD approach.

However, while this approach is ethically more attractive, it is very difficult to implement in practice. This is because it assumes a very simple approach to local peoples or communities (Figure 2.5). In reality, communities are not homogeneous and rarely speak with one voice. Community members are likely to have many different and sometimes conflicting interests.

Figure 2.5 The Batwa people living next to Bwindi Impenetrable National Park

Summary of Section 2

This section has considered the pressures on land from humans and wildlife, which sometimes lead to conflict. It has looked at what conservation is and why and how it is done. Approaches to conservation and the management of human–wildlife conflict have been shown to change over space and time. Two approaches to conservation have been discussed, fortress conservation and integrated conservation and development.

The following sections explore how these conflicting interests are negotiated and accommodated through a real world example, the Bwindi Impenetrable National Park.

3 Bwindi Impenetrable National Park case study

Bwindi Impenetrable National Park

The conservation of the mountain gorillas of Bwindi and the development of the people that live around the forest are the subject of the case study that makes up the rest of Part 2. This is delivered on the course DVD and includes videos and other resources.

The Bwindi case study on the course DVD forms a substantial part of the study for Block 3. You should work through it at your own pace, a section at a time, in the same way as you would for book-based study. On the course calendar there are nearly two weeks allocated for this case study so you need to plan for a significant amount of time working with your computer.

Summary of Part 2

This brief return to the Block 3 book serves to bring the block to a close.

Part 2 has discussed wildlife conservation and, by close examination of the gorillas in Bwindi, has explored the complexity of planning and managing wildlife conservation in a real world situation.

After completing Part 2 you should be able to:

- recognise that attitudes and approaches to conservation change over time and space
- appreciate that destruction of habitat is a threat to species biodiversity
- consider the competing claims of different stakeholders that give rise to human-wildlife conflict
- explore strategies for conserving biodiversity
- use a range of materials to evaluate evidence and develop an argument
- carry out a limited web search for a specified purpose.

Block 3 has focused on the Nile basin and principally on the people who live there and their relationship with their environment. The title of the block, Nile limits, acknowledges that the communities featured in the block, in Ethiopia and Uganda, lie at the geographical limits of the Nile basin. It also reflects the lives of the people, many of whom live in situations where basic survival has to be their top priority. They are frequently in competition for limited resources both with each other and with their environment. The block has shown that although the issues are complex and difficult, and there are many barriers to success, with negotiation, cooperation and understanding, it should be possible to achieve acceptable and sustainable outcomes.

Block 3 has also used two different delivery methods for study and learning. Increasingly study material for distance learning is provided on a computer screen rather than on the printed page. Whether you prefer computer-based or book-based study is very much a matter of personal taste but this block has made extensive use of the course DVD to add to your experience of this method of learning.

References

BC Spaces (2008) *The History of Conservation*, http://www.spacesfornature.org/greatspaces/conservation.html (Accessed 12 February 2008).

Child, B. (1993) 'The Elephant as a Natural Resource: A Perspective from Zimbabwe', *Wildlife Conservation*, vol. 96, no. 2, pp. 60–61.

Fossey, D. (1985) *Gorillas in the Mist*, London, Penguin Books.

Sigmar, G. (2007) 'Biodiversity fundamental to economics', 9 March, http://news.bbc.co.uk/1/hi/sci/tech/6432217.stm (Accessed 9 March 2007).

Siurua, H. (2006) 'Nature above people, Rolston and 'Fortress' conservation in the South', *Ethics and the Environment*, vol. 11, no. 1, pp. 71–96.

Acknowledgements

Grateful acknowledgement is made to the following sources:

Text

Page 56: McCully, P. (2001) Silenced Rivers: The Ecology and Politics of Large Dams, Zed Books, London & New York; Page 62: Walsh, C.M. and Shalita, S. (2007) Uganda's President, the Aga Khan, Cut ribbon on Bujagali Dam Project, The World Bank. Courtesy of the World Bank; Page 64: Rice, X. (2007) White water torrent to die as nation gambles on huge Nile dam project, *The Guardian*, May 31st 2007. Copyright Guardian News & Media Ltd. 2007.

Tables

Table 1.1: Gleick, P.H. (2000) *The World's Water*, Island Press;

Figures

Figures 1.1a, b and c: Courtesy of Richard Adams; Figure 1.2: Adapted from a map by Map Design Unit, World Bank; Figure 1.3: Courtesy NASA/ GSFC/MITI/ERSDAC/JAROS and US/Japan Visualization. Taken from http://visibleearth.nasa.gov; Figure 1.6: Adapted from Mather & Chapman (1995) Environmental Resources training pack, Longman Group; Figure 1.7a: © Corbis Premium RF/Alamy; Figure 1.7b: Courtesy of Rolla City Waste Water Dept., Missouri; Figure 1.8: From www.flickr.com/Ina Jura; Figure 1.9: © iStockphoto; Figure 1.10: Courtesy of International Fund for Agricultural Development (IFAD)/Alberto Conti; Figure 1.12c: © Caroline Irby/WaterAid; Figure 1.16a: www.copix.co.uk/Christine Osborne; Figure 1.16b: Courtesy of Thorkild Schioler/Experimentarium; Figure 1.17: © NASA Modis; Figure 1.18a: © Michael S. Lewis/Corbis; Figure 1.18b: Used under Creative Commons licence from www.flickr.com/sarahemcc; Figure 1.19a: © Rolf Richardson/Alamy; Figure 1.19b: © Matthew Corke; Figures 1.19c, 1.20, 1.22b and 1.25: © Pamela Furniss; Figure 1.22a: Bank of Ethiopia; Figure 1.23: © Images of Africa Photobank/ Alamy; Figure 1.24a: Courtesy of Hochtief, Germany; Figure 1.24b: © Sandro Vannini/Corbis; Figure 1.27: Taken from www.wikipedia.org; Figure 1.30: Taken from www.gharainwater.org; Figure 1.31: Wetlands taken from www.african-bush-bard.com, shoe bill © Martin Harvey/ Corbis.

Figure 2.1: Courtesy of UK Biodiversity Policy Unit/DEFRA; Figure 2.2: Hackaert, J. and Berchem, N. A Stag Hunt in a Forest/The National Gallery Picture Library; Figure 2.3: Courtesy of National Park Service, US Department of the Interior; Figure 2.4: Courtesy of The Dian Fossey Fund International, www.gorillafund.org; Figure 2.5: Courtesy of Belinda Kirk.

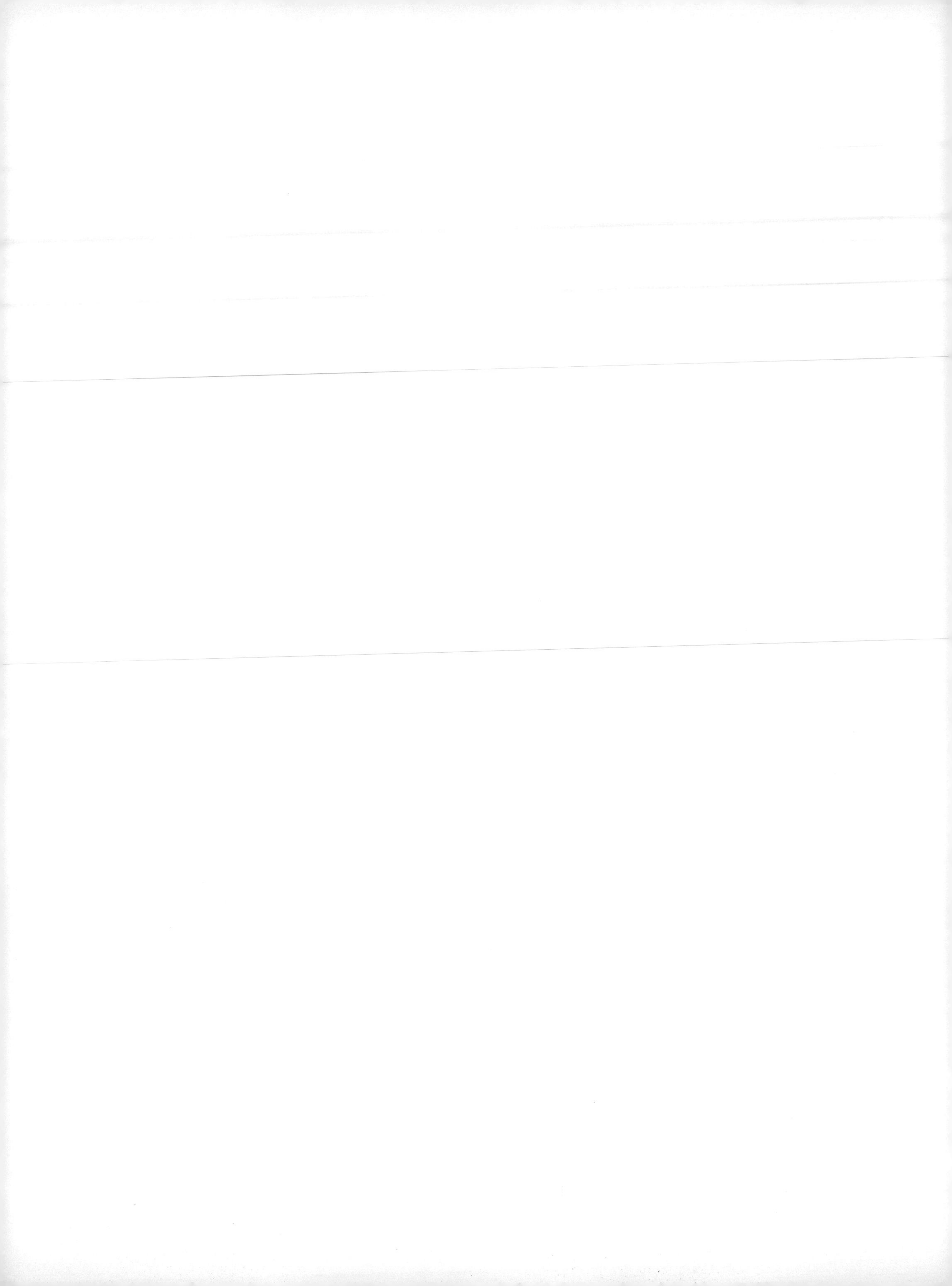